LEARN TO **LEAD**

CIVIL AIR PATROL CADET PROGRAMS

"Only the man who knows how to obey can understand what it is to command and give orders when the spears are coming at him and his time to lead has come."

SOPHOCLES

"There are no secrets to success. It is the result of preparation, hard work, and learning from failure."

COLIN POWELL

"Few men are willing to brave . . . the wrath of their society. Moral courage is a rarer commodity than bravery in battle."

ROBERT F. KENNEDY

"Only those who will risk going too far can possibly find out how far one can go."

T.S. ELIOT

"The medals don't mean anything and the glory doesn't last. It's all about your happiness."

JACKIE JOYNER-KERSEE

"Miss Jean Louise, stand up. Your father's passin'."

HARPER LEE

MAJOR **S. ROCHELLE "LEX" KIMBRELL**, USAF
FIRST BLACK FEMALE FIGHTER PILOT &
FORMER CAP CADET

LEARN TO LEAD
Published by Civil Air Patrol
Maxwell Air Force Base, Ala.

CURT LAFOND
with Associate Editors
NEIL PROBST & BECCI SUNDHAGEN

LEARN TO **LEAD**

CIVIL AIR PATROL CADET PROGRAMS

CONTENTS

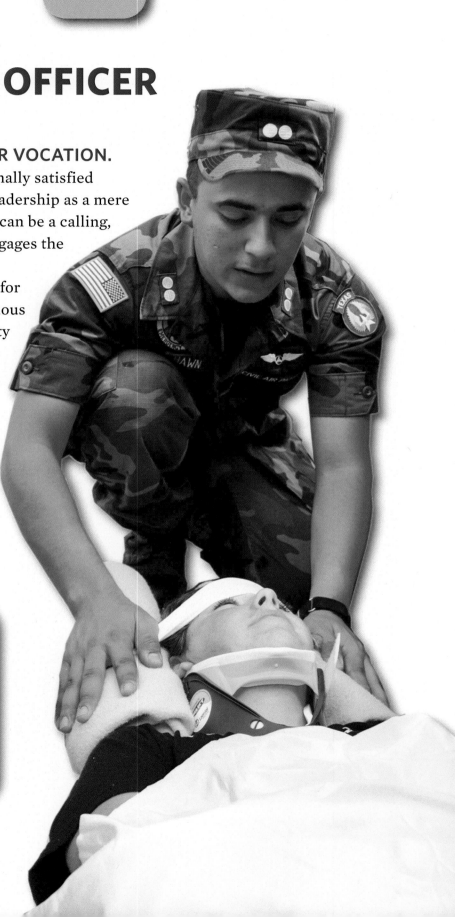

9

CHAPTER 9
THE CADET OFFICER

LEADERSHIP CAN BE YOUR VOCATION.
The most successful and personally satisfied professionals do not think of leadership as a mere occupation. Rather, leadership can be a calling, a vocation, a profession that engages the heart, mind, and soul.

What might be the "calling" for cadet officers? Perhaps continuous self-development, or community service, or the mentoring of younger cadets, or all three challenges and more.

The first section of this chapter examines the history of the officer corps and the view that leadership can be a vocation.

CHAPTER GOALS

1. Appreciate the opportunities and responsibilities of officership.

2. Recognize the officer's challenge to be a moral leader and teacher.

3. Understand the leader's role in resolving conflict.

OFFICERSHIP

HISTORY OF THE OFFICER CORPS

OBJECTIVES:

1. Describe how officers' professional expectations rose with the birth of the modern military.
2. Discuss how the concept of a meritocracy guides militaries in the selection of officers.

Weak Leaders in Command. Today, the U.S. military's officer corps is respected tremendously within the armed forces and by the public at large. But for centuries, military officers were not respected for their special knowledge and skills. In fact, the concept of an officer – that is a professional, an expert soldier, a true and learned leader – was not to be found in any nation until the early 1800s.

> *"Wealth, birth, personal and political influence dictated the appointment and advancement of officers. Children and incompetents frequently held high military rank. Nobody of professional knowledge existed. Consequently, no institutions, except for a few technical schools, were available to impart military knowledge, and there was no system for applying that knowledge in practice. Officers behaved and believed like aristocrats... In brief, the military profession was simply nonexistent."[1]*

Career Officers
The generals who won WWII were all career officers who possessed formal military training and climbed the ranks via their merit as leaders. Here, seated left to right are Simpson, Patton, Spaatz, Eisenhower, Bradley, Hodges, and Gerow; standing are Stearley, Vandenberg, Smith, Weyland, and Nugent.

Rise of the Meritocracy. Why did nations abandon the idea that who your father was or how much money you had would be the most important considerations in selecting officers? After the American and French revolutions, egalitarian ideals took root. Wealth and ancestry, and later race and gender, no longer were viewed as fair or honorable measures of a leader. Each individual is equal, at least in dignity. Egalitarian ideas naturally led to the concept of the meritocracy. In a meritocracy, merit rules. The smartest, most creative, most expert, most accomplished individuals are able to rise to the top and earn the most prestigious and rewarding positions.

egalitarian
Relating to the principle that all people are equal and deserve equal rights and opportunities.

Rise of Technology. At the same time that old biases fell to egalitarian and meritocratic ideals, warfare become more complicated. The 19th century gave rise to the Industrial Revolution, producing game-changing new technologies. Military leaders realized that to master new technologies like iron-clad ships, rifling, flintlock cannons, mechanically-fused land mines, railroads, battlefield medicine, and more, officers would have to undergo specialized training. Any random rich son of a prominent father wouldn't necessarily be suited to the demands of the increasingly technical and complex demands of military leadership. Officers were not born; rather, they were educated and trained for the profession of arms.

The Service Academies
The United States maintains service academies to train and educate an officer corps. The academies reflect the ideals of an officer corps constituted upon merit, not birthright.

Birth of the Modern Officer Corps. The rise of the meritocracy and the new complexity of warfare gave birth to the concept of the modern officer corps. This Prussian government decree from 1808 summarizes that new view of officership, a view that remains dominant even today:

> *"The only title to an officer's commission shall be, in time of peace, education and professional knowledge; in time of war, distinguished valor and perception. From the entire nation, therefore, all individuals who possess these qualities are eligible for the highest military posts. All previously existing class preference in the military establishment is abolished, and every man, without regard to his origins, has equal duties and equal rights."[2]*

USMA West Point

USNA Annapolis

USCGA New London

USAFA Colorado Springs

OATH & COMMISSION

OBJECTIVE:

3. Defend the requirement for officers to swear an oath of office.

Where do officers come from? Air Force doctrine talks of leaders being made through experience, education, and training.[3] But what mechanism creates an officer? The U.S. Constitution declares, "the President... shall commission all the officers of the United States."[4] Because of this constitutional principle, new officers first make an oath of office and then receive a certificate of commission.

The oath of office professes what an officer will do and to whom she will swear her allegiance. Responsibility should always accompany authority, so the oath (a profession of responsibility) comes before the actual commission. In 21st-century America, it's easy to take the oath's principles for granted. Thankfully, we've never experienced a group of rogue military officers conspiring to overthrow the republic.

The oath's key principle is the officer's promise to support the Constitution against all enemies. Recall that in chapter 1 we discussed how armies of the Old World swore allegiance to their particular lord or general. Although the president is the military's commander in chief, officers do not pledge to do whatever they want; rather, even the president's authority is circumscribed by the Constitution.

circumscribe
To restrict within certain limits.

Each officer is commissioned. That is, they receive a legal document designating them as officers and granting them authority to lead. Again, it's easy to take this concept for granted. "You're an officer? Who says?" The president delegates authority to the officer through the certificate of commission. This physical document is a visible sign of the president's trust in the individual officer and the basis for that officer's authority.

Having professed the oath of office and received a commission, the Code of Conduct – the warfighter's essential duties – now compels the officer "to guard our country and our way of life, and to give [his] life in [its] defense."[5]

THE PRESIDENT OF THE UNITED STATES OF AMERICA

To all who shall see these presents greeting:
Know ye, reposing special trust and confidence in the patriotism, valor, fidelity and abilities of (Full Name), I do appoint Him/Her, **Second Lieutenant** in the

UNITED STATES AIR FORCE

as such from the (number) day of (month), (year).

This officer will therefore carefully and diligently discharge the duties of the office to which appointed by doing and performing all manner of things thereunto belonging. And I do strictly charge and require those officers and other personnel of lesser rank to render such obedience as is due an officer of this grade and position. And this officer is to observe and follow such orders and directions from time to time, as may be given by the President of the United States of America, or other superior officers acting in accordance with the laws of the United States of America. This commission is to continue in force during the pleasure of the President of the United States of America under the provisions of those public laws relating to officers of the Armed Forces of the United States of America and the component thereof in which this appointment is made. Signed by the Secretary of the Air Force as delegated by the President of the United States of America.[6]

OATH OF OFFICE

I (name), having been appointed a (grade), United States Air Force, do solemnly swear (or affirm) that I will support and defend the Constitution of the United States against all enemies, foreign and domestic; that I will bear true faith and allegiance to the same; that I take this obligation freely, without any mental reservation or purpose of evasion; and that I will well and faithfully discharge the duties of the office upon which I am about to enter, (so help me God).[7]

PATHS TO A COMMISSION

This table shows the path that new active duty lieutenants and ensigns followed to obtain a commission in all branches in 2009:[8]

Service Academy	17%	
ROTC Scholarship	18%	
ROTC Non-Scholarship	12%	
Officer Training School	29%	(about 20% of these are prior enlisted)
Direct Appointment	17%	(lawyers, physicians, chaplains, etc.)
Other / Unknown	7%	

In 2011, the Air Force awarded ROTC scholarships to students pursuing the following majors:[9]

Scientific or technical field of study	70%
Foreign language	20%
All other majors	10%

Profile of the "average" AFROTC scholarship recipient:[10]

Class Rank	Top 12%
Grade Point Average	3.77
SAT	1260 (out of 1600)
ACT	27

Per tradition, newly-minted officers present a silver dollar to the first enlisted person who salutes them

THE OFFICER CORPS TODAY

Officers are professional leaders, entrusted with serious responsibility. Officership has evolved. More than ever, America demands that its officers be highly educated. One Secretary of Defense put it this way:

> *"Once it was enough that the military leader excel in strength and stamina and courage. The range of talents required of [officers today] is infinitely broader...We need military leaders who understand this complex world in which we live... the scientific revolution... the techniques of managing bafflingly complex organizations... combined with qualities of character that inspire others..."[11]*

The cadet officer's task then is to try to emulate these hallmarks of officership. Though not legally bound by an oath of office or formally commissioned by the President, cadet officers can still think of themselves as pursuing a vocation of leadership and service.

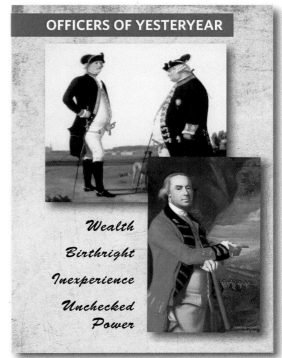

OFFICERS OF YESTERYEAR

Wealth

Birthright

Inexperience

Unchecked Power

TODAY'S OFFICERS: "INFINITELY BROADER TALENTS"

INSPIRATIONAL LEADERSHIP

adaptability for a complex world

a range of talents

CHARACTER

scientific competency

PORTRAIT OF AN OFFICER: MASON MATHIAS[12]

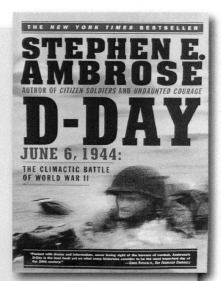

Lt Robert Mason Mathias was the leader of the second platoon, E Company, 508th Parachute Infantry Regiment, U.S. 82nd Airborne Division. At midnight, June 5/6, 1944, he was riding in a C-47 Dakota over the English Channel, headed toward the Cotentin Peninsula of Normandy.

> **Lt Mathias discreetly offered his counsel, but never intruded. He made allowances, but never compromised his standards.**

The Germans below were firing furiously at the air armada of 822 C-47s carrying the 82nd and 101st Airborne divisions into battle . . . As the C-47 lurched this way and that, a consequence of the pilot's futile attempts to escape the flak, the men behind Mathias were calling out, "Let's go," or "Jump, damn it, jump."

Mathias had his hands on the outside of the doorway, ready to propel himself into the night the instant the green light went on. A shell burst just beside him. Red-hot flak ripped through his reserve chute into his chest, knocking him off his feet. With a mighty effort, he began to pull himself back up. The green light went on.

It was the kind of action his men had learned to expect from Bob Mathias. He was immensely popular

> **Bob Mathias was absolutely fair, totally dedicated. On a 25-mile march, one of his men gave out. Mathias picked him up and carried him home.**

with his platoon and fellow officers. For two years he had been preparing himself and his platoon for this moment. He was known to be absolutely fair, totally dedicated. He was the best boxer in the regiment, and the best marcher. On one twenty-five-mile march, an intraplatoon competitive hike, when everyone was pushing the limit, one of his men gave out. Mathias picked him up and carried him the last three-quarters of a mile home.

Mathias was a devout Catholic. He went to Mass as often as possible and did all he could to make church attendance convenient for his men. He never swore. His company commander said of him, "He can hold more than his own with the toughest man alive; yet you won't ever hear him use hell or damn."

When a man in the second platoon had a problem, Mathias could sense it. He would discreetly offer his counsel, but he never intruded. One of his privates recalled, "He made allowances, but never compromised his standards. He seemed deeply hurt on the few occasions we failed to meet his expectations, but he never lost his temper."

He had prepared himself in every way possible for the upcoming struggle. He was a student of military history. He had mastered every weapon and skill necessary to a rifle company. He had studied German weapons, organization, and tactics. He had learned the German language well enough to speak it fluently, and French well enough to ask directions. He had taught his men German commands and French phrases. "Valuable lessons," Cavanaugh remarked.

> **"Follow me!"**

When Lieutenant Mathias was wounded from the shell burst and the green light went on, he had enough strength to push himself out of the way, so that the men behind him could jump. Had he done so, the crew of the C-47 could have applied first aid and —perhaps — gotten him back to England in time for a life-saving operation. Later, every man in his stick was certain that Mathias must have had that thought.

Instead, Mathias raised his right arm, called out "Follow me!" and leaped into the night. Whether the shock from the opening parachute, or the shock of hitting the ground, or excessive bleeding from his multiple wounds was the cause, no one knows, but when he was located a half hour or so later, he was still in his chute, dead. He was the first American officer killed by German fire on D-Day.

Excerpted from Stephen E. Ambrose, *D-Day, June 6, 1944: The Climactic Battle of World War II,* (New York: Touchstone, 1995), 22-24.
ISBN: 0-671-67334-3
Reprinted with permission.

INDIRECT LEADERSHIP

OBJECTIVE:

4.   Compare and contrast direct leadership with indirect leadership.

When you became an NCO, you transitioned from "one who is cared for to one who cares for others."[13] Now as a cadet officer, you must transition from the tactical to operational arena, from one who leads directly to one who leads in concert with and through other leaders. Being a mid- to high-level leader in an organization requires skill in indirect leadership.

As a new cadet officer, does your changing leadership role mean less fun and excitement? No, it's just the opposite. You'll enjoy increased authority, tougher challenges, and an opportunity to make a bigger impact on the team. All told, your leadership experiences will really make you stand out in life when compared with your non-cadet peers. It's only now as a cadet officer that you'll truly begin to mature as a leader.

See chapter 4 for a review of the leadership arenas: strategic, operational, and tactical.

This section discusses the concept of indirect leadership. The closely related issue of how to delegate authority will be discussed in chapter 11.

FORMS OF INDIRECT LEADERSHIP

OBJECTIVES:

5.   Describe the four forms of indirect leadership.
6.   Explain what the term "link" means in the context of indirect leadership.
7.   Defend the principle that upward influence can be a positive form of indirect leadership.

Indirect leadership is visible in at least four forms: leadership from a distance, leadership through a link, leadership through creations, and upward influence.

Leadership from a Distance. Leaders who are concerned with the development and performance of individuals who do not directly report to them are said to be indirect leaders who lead from a distance.[14] Take a cadet representative to the wing Cadet Advisory Council, for instance. CAC representatives hope to influence the wing's cadet corps. They have no command authority over those cadets. If the wing is large, it's unlikely that the representatives will even meet every single cadet whom they hope to affect. Still, by speaking out on cadet issues and advising the wing commander on how to make the Cadet Program better, the representatives are leaders: indirect leaders working from a distance.

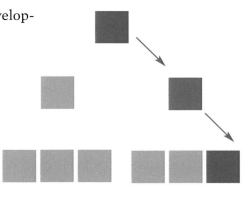

An illustration of leadership through a link. Here, the blue leader represents the link through which the top red leader exerts influence.

Leadership through a Link. Leaders who work through subordinate leaders are indirect leaders. The military-style chain of command familiar to cadets is a great example. Squadron commanders lead through flight commanders and element leaders in an effort to influence the in-ranks cadets. In this example, the flight commanders and element leaders are the "links" who relay messages to lower levels.

Indirect leadership then requires less task-related competence and more conceptual skills (the leadership matrix presented in chapter 4 illustrates this point).[15] Researchers found that leading through a link means you can't be there to personally direct every subordinate all the time, so your personnel selections are important. "We try to direct through picking the right people," observed one military officer.[16] Another added, "I'm not so spontaneous and direct as I was before."[17] Indirect leaders have to be more thoughtful and self-controlling than direct leaders. Therefore, it's no surprise that in decision-making, indirect leaders who work through a link are more cautious and deliberative. One officer explains, "It may be the case that I need to know more before I [make decisions and] confirm that it's OK to go ahead."[18]

Leadership through Creations. Artists, philosophers, inventors, poets, and the like lead indirectly. Mark Zuckerberg's Facebook revolutionized how people stay in touch, and yet apart from Facebook's employees, he's not the boss of anybody. Leaders of this stripe make their influence felt indirectly, through the symbolic products they create.[19] No surprise that one expert believes indirect leadership requires comfort with chaos. Chaos signifies "freedom and productivity, while direct leadership is terrified by disorder."[20]

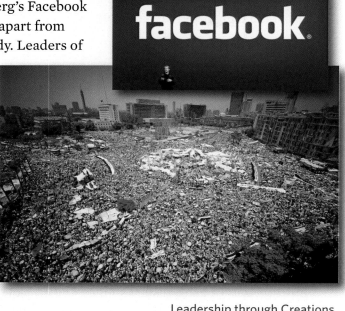

Even formal leaders like corporate executives can lead indirectly through creations. After all, the indirect leaders who sit atop big organizations use slogans, logos, and mission statements to steer culture, just like musicians and writers do in their own way as indirect leaders.

> "Through the use of organizational stories, rites and rituals, symbols, slogans, logos and other cultural elements, the leader provides...a picture of the organization. As the definers and givers of culture, leaders set the tone, atmosphere, and philosophy for the organizations...Leaders are the source of cues about reality, expectations, and information for others at levels removed from him or her."[21]

Leadership through Creations
Mark Zuckerberg transformed social life, and his creation - Facebook - helped people organize the "Arab Spring" revolutions. Pictured above, protestors in Cairo's Tahrir Square demand President Hosni Mubarak's resignation in 2011.

Upward Influence. The best leaders are so expert they are able to influence even their boss. Think of upward influence simply as direct leadership in reverse – the subordinate leads the superior, instead of vice versa. Thus, leadership can be "top-down and direct, and bottom-up and indirect."[22] And why shouldn't a leader be receptive to influence from a follower? Maybe that follower has the right idea. Upward influence will be seen only in organizations where bosses truly show they are willing to listen to subordinates, and when those subordinates are truly made to feel that their input is valued.[23]

One comic example of upward influence is found in the old sitcom *Hogan's Heroes*, set in a German prisoner of war camp during WWII. The Allies, led by Colonel Hogan, are guarded by a bumbling incompetent, Sergeant Schultz. Through misdirection, the power of suggestion, reverse psychology, and other tricks, Col Hogan makes Sgt Schultz inadvertently reveal secret information or carry out some innocuous task that makes it easy for our heroes to sneak in and out of camp and sabotage the Nazi war effort. In truth, Col. Hogan's antics are examples of manipulations, not pure leadership, but the basic point remains. The POWs exerted an upward influence upon their captors / superiors.

I know nothing! Nothing!

CHARACTERISTICS *of* INDIRECT LEADERSHIP [24]

Two-way communication is more difficult for indirect leaders
The colonel is physically separated from the airman; captains and sergeants are intervening links between the colonel and the airman

The indirect leader and follower are less likely to know one another personally
With one hundred or more cadets at a summer encampment, the cadet commander might meet every single cadet, but won't really know each cadet individually

The number of followers per leader increase
The colonel is an indirect leader of several hundred airmen, but a direct leader to a handful of majors

Fewer short-term issues are to be resolved by indirect leaders
Direct leaders handle short-term, on-the-spot, routine issues

Spontaneous action and reaction are impossible for indirect leaders
The CAP National Commander wants everyone to tune in to a special report on tonight's news, but getting that message out to 60,000 members takes a lot of time

The indirect leader is faced with problems beyond his or her control
The colonel can't be on scene to ensure every airman is properly trained; he or she has to trust the direct leaders and the system to work as designed

The AIR FORCE SYMBOL *as a* LEADERSHIP TOOL

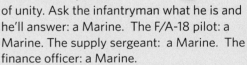

"Once a Marine, always a Marine." "The few, the proud, the Marines."

Those slogans have instant recognition, and moreover, a sense of unity. Ask the infantryman what he is and he'll answer: a Marine. The F/A-18 pilot: a Marine. The supply sergeant: a Marine. The finance officer: a Marine.

Air Force Chief of Staff Gen Michael Ryan looked with admiration upon how a single culture permeates the Marine Corps. But he believed the Air Force lacked that instant brand recognition.

Moreover, Gen. Ryan worried that because the Air Force never formally adopted an official symbol, logos like the Strategic Air Command's gauntlet and lightning bolts or the Tactical Air Command's winged sword had more influence on the troops than the master brand.[25]

Who cares? What's it matter which logos are seen most often? Gen Ryan found that the lack of an official Air Force symbol resulted in people identifying themselves as, "I'm fighter mafia," or "I'm a missileer," never the more unifying label, "I'm an Airman."

Therefore, Gen Ryan ordered the creation of the Air Force Symbol. As an indirect leader, he used that creation, that cultural element, to unify the "total force."

A single, ubiquitous Air Force Symbol set a new tone for the organization.

IMPLICATIONS FOR CADET OFFICERS

What do the principles of indirect leadership mean to you as a cadet officer? Your leadership role is changing. You'll need to learn how to lead others from a distance, to lead through a staff of NCOs, to lead through creations and innovations, and to employ an upward influence on your boss. In short, an entirely new set of leadership skills are needed as you transition from straightforward direct leadership to the more complex, challenging, and rewarding form of indirect leadership.

PUBLIC TRUST

OBJECTIVE:

8. Explain why organizations and leaders are expected to honor a public trust.

"...That to secure these rights, Governments are instituted among Men, deriving their just powers from the consent of the governed..."
THE DECLARATION OF INDEPENDENCE

"If men were angels, no government would be necessary."
MADISON, FEDERALIST 51

Power requires consent. The entire American civilization, not only American government, is built upon the belief that just powers (that is, all powers that are morally right and fair) come from the consent of the governed. The public rules.

Taken more broadly, leaders who find themselves in powerful positions have an obligation to the public at large. Even private companies are subject to scrutiny. Because men are not angels (to borrow from Madison), the public, the news media, watchdog groups, and the courts take an interest in the actions of organizations and the leaders who head them. (See *Deepwater Horizon spill, BP*. See *$182 billion bailout, AIG*. See *crash, ValueJet flight 592*, etc.)

America expects its organizations and leaders to honor the public trust.

Deepwater Horizon
The actions of a private company, BP, lead to a major disaster called "Deepwater Horizon." An offshore oil rig exploded. For three months, oil flowed unabated, affecting the US Gulf Coast region. As a result of the massive disaster, BP lost the trust of an outraged public.

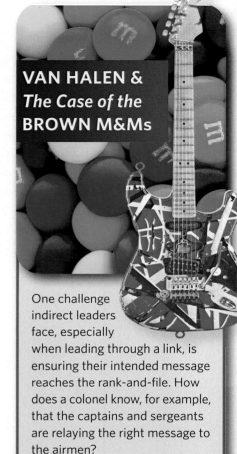

VAN HALEN & *The Case of the* BROWN M&Ms

One challenge indirect leaders face, especially when leading through a link, is ensuring their intended message reaches the rank-and-file. How does a colonel know, for example, that the captains and sergeants are relaying the right message to the airmen?

The classic rock band Van Halen believed they faced such a situation. So much goes into a rock concert: lighting, sound systems, security, ticketing, and maybe even dangerous pyrotechnics.

Therefore, Van Halen buried a special requirement in the fine print of its contract. The concert promoter had to provide the band with M&Ms to snack on, but *"absolutely no brown M&Ms"* could be included.[26] In other words, a low-level backstage staffer would have to buy a bag of M&Ms, then manually find all the brown ones and toss them out (or eat them himself)!

Why? Van Halen reasoned that by checking their M&M supply, they could quickly see if the concert promoters were paying close attention to the band's instructions. A bowl full of non-brown M&Ms meant the promoters were prepared and Van Halen could perform a great show.

CORPORATE SOCIAL RESPONSIBILITY

OBJECTIVE:

9.   Describe sample issues relating to corporate social responsibility.

Corporate social responsibility (CSR) is a term describing this intersection between corporations and the public trust. Some organizations prefer the term "corporate citizenship." CSR is "how companies manage the business processes to produce an overall positive impact on society."[27] CSR principles state that corporate executives have a duty to run their business "in a manner that meets or exceeds the ethical, legal, commercial, and public expectations that society has of business."[28] It's worth noting that CSR principles are self-imposed, not generally mandated by law. What are some CSR issues?

Corruption. Corruption is the abuse of entrusted power for private gain.[29] It's the antithesis of "Service Before Self." Perhaps the most familiar form of corruption is bribery, but it's also seen when a leader pockets the group's money, and in conflicts of interest when a leader allows his or her personal interests to interfere with what's best for the organization.

Stewardship. All members of an organization, especially its officers or leaders, are expected to be good stewards of the organization's resources. Stewardship involves the careful management of what is not yours. When a CAP pilot treats a $550,000 rescue-equipped *Skylane* as if it were her own, she is practicing good stewardship. A for-profit example would be an executive taking care to manage the company so that it will continue to succeed for years to come, even if that means sacrificing short-term gains for long-term stability.

Philanthropy. Today, corporations go to great lengths to share their profits with worthy charities. *Forbes* magazine, famous for compiling an annual list of the 400 richest individuals on earth, is also compiling an annual ranking of the most generous corporations. Whether companies give because they truly want to or because it makes them look good, the result is the same: good causes win.

Sustainability. Sustainability or green business is a key issue in CSR. Sustainability means the organization acknowledges the limits of nature and tries to take a long-term systems view as to how it impacts the environment.[30] Hikers have long been familiar with the sustainability concept through their "leave no trace" mantra. In the for-profit world, Subaru won enormous praise for committing one of its factories to a zero-landfill policy: any waste left over after making cars is either recycled, reused, or converted to energy.[31]

CSR Matters
According to *Forbes*, the business magazine, the top three most generous companies in 2011 were Kroger, Macy's, and Safeway.[32] The fact that *Forbes* tracks corporate generosity illustrates the growing importance of CSR.

Human Rights. If you sell a product, are you responsible for how that product was made? Ask talk show host Kathie Lee Gifford. Her clothing line was revealed to be manufactured using child laborers under deplorable conditions in Honduras. The public outcry was huge, especially because Mrs. Gifford had been admired as a sunny, wholesome TV personality. She ordered her manufacturers to change their ways. Claiming a human rights victory, one activist said, "The whole Kathie Lee [scandal] literally changed the way people do business."[33]

Kathie Lee Gifford
The upbeat TV personality did not know her line of clothing was being made in sweatshop conditions.

Transparency. "Sunlight is said to be the best of disinfectants," wrote one Supreme Court justice; "electric light the most efficient policeman."[34] Transparency is the principle that those affected by a business or organization should be allowed to know about its operations and practices.[35] Because of the principle of transparency, organizations have their funds audited so stockholders or taxpayers or donors can see how their money was spent. Political contributions are a matter of public record in the U.S., because of a belief that transparency in campaigns leads to good government. CAP routinely streams its board meetings live over the web, in respect for the principle of transparency.

CSR CASE STUDY: THE TYLENOL MURDERS

It's 1982 and you're Tylenol's chief executive. You're told that seven people have died after having taken your popular medicine. Why? A madman has laced the pills with deadly cyanide.

The FBI learns that the poisoning had taken place after the Tylenol reached the shelves of Chicago-area supermarkets. Surely your company can't be blamed for what happens to Tylenol after it leaves your factory. And how many other bottles of Tylenol in Chicago, in Illinois, in the United States have been poisoned? No one knows.

What do you do?

Johnson & Johnson, the makers of Tylenol, made their decision. They voluntarily recalled all 31 million bottles of the medicine from every shelf in every store across America. The recall cost them over $100 million.[36] Why? It was the right thing to do. Before shipping Tylenol products back to stores, the bottles were redesigned with three layers of protective packaging.

Johnson & Johnson exceeded the public's ethical and legal expectations for a drug company, and in so doing, set a new standard for corporate social responsibility.

PROFESSIONAL RESPONSIBILITY

OBJECTIVES:

10. Describe why professionals often join professional associations.
11. Explain why most professional associations adopt a code of ethics.

Professionalism, if you recall from chapter 4, is not the job you do but how you do it. In their efforts to honor the public trust, professionals join professional associations. A professional association is a group that seeks to further a certain career field, help members succeed in that profession, and uphold the public trust. Airmen might join the Air Force Association, businesspeople might join the American Management Association, and engineers could join the American Institute of Aeronautics and Astronautics.

One way professional associations advance their field and earn the public's trust is by adopting a professional code of ethics. Sometimes aspirational, sometimes prescriptive, codes of ethics identify moral standards that all members of the profession are expected to honor.[37] While CAP and the Air Force have Core Values, professional codes of ethics tend to be less general and more particular about the ethical issues one can expect to encounter in a particular profession. For example, a code for psychiatrists will certainly address patient confidentiality. A code for zoologists will undoubtedly address how animals are to be treated when conducting scientific research.

Leaders who think of themselves as professionals will naturally see merit in their profession adopting a code of ethics. But self-interest plays a part, too. Groups that do not adopt codes of ethics or police themselves are more likely to become vulnerable to external regulation. The movie rating system is a good example. Ratings are not matters of law, but ethical practices that the studios and theaters pledge to uphold. If Hollywood had not created a movie rating system, it's likely that many local governments would have created a patchwork of regulations, with each town censoring films in its own way.[38]

But if membership in a professional association is voluntary, how do codes of ethics really work? Some professionals, such as attorneys, are required to belong to an association and to follow that group's code in order to maintain their license to practice law. Deviate from the bar association's code of ethics and your livelihood is in jeopardy. In other professions, leaders who fall short of the code's requirements might be censured or reprimanded, assigned remedial courses in ethics, or be expelled from the group.[39] Social stigma can be a powerful motivator.

Not illegal, but still wrong:
PROFESSIONAL MISCONDUCT

Not all misdeeds are crimes. Presented below are four notable tales of highly successful professionals whose colleagues rebuked them for professional misconduct.

Journalist Jayson Blair of the *New York Times* was discovered to have made-up several of his news stories. *Times* editors were so embarassed by the scandal they published a 7,000-word apology and correction of his reporting. The *Times* demanded his and his boss's resignation.[40]

Historian Doris Kearns Goodwin failed to properly credit her sources when writing a book about the Kennedy family. Although an unintentional error, the incident brought discredit to the Pullitzer Prize-winning author.[41]

Marion Jones won five Olympic medals in track and field, but upon her testing positive for performance-enhancing drugs, she was called a "cheat" and made to forfeit her three Gold and two Bronze medals.[42]

The US Congress voted to reprimand Rep. Joe Wilson for shouting "You lie!" during President Obama's speech to a Joint Session of Congress. The House said his outburst "degraded its proceedings."[43]

CODES OF ETHICS

Shown below are sample codes of ethics, taken verbatim from major professional associations.

Airline Pilot[44]

An airline pilot will keep uppermost in his mind that the safety, comfort, and well-being of the passengers who entrust their lives to him are his first and greatest responsibility.

• He will never permit external pressures or personal desires to influence his judgment, nor will he knowingly do anything that could jeopardize flight safety.

• He will remember that an act of omission can be as hazardous as a deliberate act of commission, and he will not neglect any detail that contributes to the safety of his flight, or perform any operation in a negligent or careless manner.

• Consistent with flight safety, he will at all times operate his aircraft in a manner that will contribute to the comfort, peace of mind, and well-being of his passengers, instilling in them trust in him and the airline he represents.

• Once he has discharged his primary responsibility for the safety and comfort of his passengers, he will remember that they depend upon him to do all possible to deliver them to their destination at the scheduled time.

• If disaster should strike, he will take whatever action he deems necessary to protect the lives of his passengers and crew.

Engineer[45]

Engineers, in the fulfillment of their professional duties, shall:

1. Hold paramount the safety, health, and welfare of the public.

2. Perform services only in areas of their competence.

3. Issue public statements only in an objective and truthful manner.

4. Act for each employer or client as faithful agents or trustees.

5. Avoid deceptive acts.

6. Conduct themselves honorably, responsibly, ethically, and lawfully so as to enhance the honor, reputation, and usefulness of the profession.

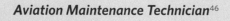

Aviation Maintenance Technician[46]

"As a certified technician, my performance is a public service and, as such, I have a responsibility to the United States Government and its citizens. I must ensure that all citizens have confidence in my integrity and that I will perform my work according to the highest principles of ethical conduct. Therefore, I swear that I shall hold in sacred trust the rights and privileges conferred upon me as a certified technician. The safety and lives of others are dependent upon my skill and judgment, therefore I shall never knowingly subject others to risks which I would not be willing to assume for myself, or for those who are dear to me."

"WE'RE GONNA BE IN THE HUDSON."

USAirways flight 1549, an Airbus A320 mid-size airliner, lost power moments after take-off from New York's LaGuardia Airport in January 2009.[47] Perhaps due to a birdstrike, both engines failed as the jet was over Manhattan with just 10,000 feet of altitude.

Listen to the audio of Captain Sully's communications with air traffic control and you won't hear any panic in his voice. As the controller quickly but confidently suggested runway options for an emergency landing, Captain Sully brushed those ideas aside with a matter of fact reply, "We're gonna be in the Hudson."

Somewhat puzzled by that declaration, the controller asks for clarification. But Captain Sully doesn't offer any. Why? He was too busy trying to prepare a fully-loaded jet for an emergency water landing.

Captain Sully's training taught him the proper ordering of priorities: (1) aviate, (2) navigate, (3) communicate.

Captain Sully's quick thinking, calm under pressure, and consummate professionalism resulted in a smooth landing on the Hudson River. His professionalism saved 155 souls on board.

We'll be okay... I'm a professional

RESPECTFUL DISSENT

OBJECTIVE:
12. Define the term "dissent."

Throughout this chapter we've emphasized that an officer owes allegiance to more than her direct supervisor. There's allegiance to the mission, allegiance to the larger organization, allegiance to the law or Constitution, allegiance to a personal code of honor, and other high callings. What happens when an officer's principles conflict with the supervisor's directions?

Dissent is the expression of opinions contrary to the official view, and a means for a leader to call attention to obligations that are higher than the duty to follow orders. Even in a military organization with a strict chain of command and concept of direct orders, dissent is a necessary feature of leadership. After all, organizations need to learn quickly, and leaders who welcome dissenting views allow useful, if unpopular, ideas to be heard.[48]

DISSENT & TEAM DYNAMICS

OBJECTIVE:

13. Explain why dissent is important for the team's success.

Thinking back to the "Abilene paradox," or the paradox of the false consensus (see chapter 4), it's clear that teams sometimes pretend to be cohesive when in reality team members harbor alternative views. People who have serious concerns about a plan of action avoid stating those dissenting views, preferring to go along with watered-down compromises.[49]

And who can blame them? It's not easy being the dissenting voice. Many individuals who go against the "official" view are punished or marginalized.[50] And in a rank-conscious environment like the military, it's natural for potential dissenters to simply keep silent.

Businesses & Government Organizations. Historians of failed businesses and crumbled civilizations have often found that knowledgeable insiders – potential dissenters – knew of the organization's weaknesses or impending doom:

> *Powerful empires collapse, often in remarkably short periods of time. Like failing organizations, most of those inside the empire sense that all is not quite right, but their instincts are to more strongly defend their traditional ways of doing things rather than to question them – let alone develop the capacity to change those ways.[51]*

Is it surprising that the Soviet Union appeared to be the number one or two superpower in the 1980s, and yet was nonexistent after 1991? Or that the stock of Wall Street giant Bear Stearns traded at $68 per share one day, but exactly one week later the firm was sold for just $2 per share? In hindsight, these collapses make perfect sense. But partly because of a culture that discourages dissent, organizations cannot easily see impending threats, nor encourage mid- or low-level leaders to express their unconventional viewpoints.[52]

Empires Crumble

(a) The British used to say the sun never set on their empire. But by the end of WWII, the UK no longer ruled over so many lands.

(b) Rome ruled nearly the entire known world. Legend has it that their Emperor Nero fiddled as the "eternal city" burned.

(c) Financial giant Bear Stearns traded at $68 per share one day, a week later $2, and then: oblivion.

(d) The Soviets built the Berlin Wall, but eventually Berliners shouted the wall down, and with it fell the "evil empire."

Might these organizations have held on to their success by heeding the advice of dissenters who forsaw the coming collapses?

DISSENT IN THE MILITARY

OBJECTIVE:

14. Defend the claim that dissent should be valued within the military.

But isn't the military special? We can't have troops questioning orders or refusing to obey them. That undermines the chain of command, right?

The Nuremberg Defense. After World War II, captured Nazi officers claimed they were innocent of war crimes because their superiors had ordered them to commit atrocities during the war. The Allies utterly rejected this so-called "Nuremburg defense" (so named because the Nazis were tried in Nuremberg, Germany). Leaders cannot escape moral responsibility for their actions simply because they were "following orders."

Still, disgraced leaders attempt to save themselves with the Nuremberg defense, only to lose every time.

Lieutenant William Calley, an Army infantry officer, was convicted of the premeditated murder of 22 residents of My Lai, a village in Vietnam, in 1968. Historians say the number of victims is actually over 500.[53] During his trial, Calley claimed his superior ordered him to shoot the civilians. The court rejected Calley's Nuremberg defense.

Nuremberg
Nazi officers defended themselves by crying, "But I was just following orders . . ." Unmoved, the world found them guilty.

Guilty
During the Vietnam War, Lt William Calley murdered civilians. His "Nuremberg defense" failed.

The Admiral Burke Award. If Calley and captured Nazis were blind to the need for dissent in the military, Admiral Arleigh Burke was not. He made a plaque and promised to award it to the first person who "knowingly disobeyed an order but did the right thing."[54]

AWARD
For knowingly disobeying an order but doing the right thing

Adm Arleigh Burke

The great strategist Napoleon understood that due to the "fog of war," lower ranking officers often have a better vantage point than the generals. Napoleon told his lieutenants that they were required to challenge the instructions of higher authority if they became aware of information that made the orders senseless.[55]

Although the military relies upon its chain of command and the duty to follow orders, the Air Force was itself born through the dissent of a single officer, Billy Mitchell. Wondering where our "Mitchells of today" can be found, one military commentator advised, "In the US, the worry may not be of losing controls to military mavericks (by allowing too much dissent), but rather a shortage of risk-taking dissent."[56]

America needs an independent AIR FORCE!

Dissenting Father
Largely because of Billy Mitchell's persistent challenges to the military thinking of his day, the United States eventually created an independent air force. The Air Force was born from dissent.

PRINCIPLES FOR RESPECTFUL DISSENT

OBJECTIVES:

15. Identify principles for dissenting with respect.
16. Identify principles for encouraging and receiving dissenting views from subordinates.

How to Respectfully Dissent. If dissent is so vital to a team, how do you dissent respectfully? Leaders offer a variety of practical advice. Use the chain of command. Stay professional and in control of your emotions. Recommend solutions; don't just complain about problems. Pick your battles, recognizing the difference between matters of style and matters of principle. And do not claim the right to criticize an idea unless you can summarize that idea in such a way that someone espousing the opposing view would admit your summary is fair.

Please listen, ma'am, I have something important to say!

How to Encourage Dissent. As an officer, you're apt to be on the receiving end of dissent, too. How do open-minded leaders handle dissent?

First, be mindful that if you outrank someone, that person could be reluctant to dissent in the first place. One expert observes, "How easy it is for a boss to send a signal that a worker should keep quiet."[57] Therefore, the leader's role is to create an environment that welcomes dissent. And, how you handle dissent today will affect whether others dare to dissent tomorrow.

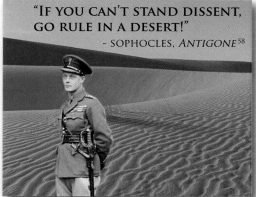

"IF YOU CAN'T STAND DISSENT, GO RULE IN A DESERT!"
- SOPHOCLES, *ANTIGONE*[58]

Practical advice includes being mindful of your stress reactions and defensive behaviors. Don't take it personally if someone challenges your views. Assume good faith. Grant that the dissenter is trying to help the team, not make trouble. Thank people for being brave enough to speak up. Better still, if you do change your view, give credit to the person who helped you see the issue in a new light. If you rarely hear dissenting views from your subordinates, ask yourself if you've been unconsciously shooting them down.

The Open Door Policy

Many leaders maintain an "open door policy," allowing everyone access to the boss. This is supposed to encourage the free flow of ideas, including dissents. But despite the promise of an "open door," people may hesitate to speak their mind. They still wonder, "Will I get into trouble for dissenting?"

This painting by Edward Hopper suggests an oceanfront "room by the sea," but if you step out that open door, will you fall into shark-infested waters?

MISTER ROGERS GOES TO CONGRESS

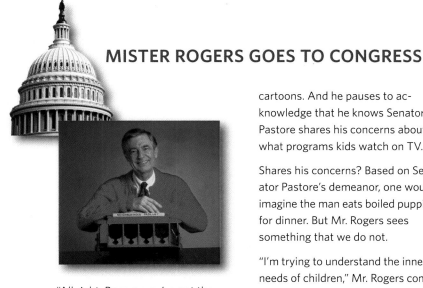

"All right, Rogers, you've got the floor." With that brusque introduction, Senator John Pastore opens a committee hearing on Capitol Hill.[59] It is 1969, and Fred Rogers is not yet the beloved, 5-time Emmy-winning star of children's educational programming. He is on Capitol Hill to ask that the PBS television network's funding be restored – $20 million for PBS overall, including a mere few thousand dollars for his own program, *Mister Rogers' Neighborhood*.

The kind man who would become a hero to millions of kids begins his testimony with disarming calmness. If a different leader were on the receiving end of Senator Pastore's abrasiveness, perhaps they would become combative, but not Mr. Rogers.

In the interest of time, Mr. Rogers volunteers to keep his remarks brief. "You've promised to read this statement later," Mr. Rogers gently reminds the senator, "and I trust what you have said, that you will read it."

When gentle Mr. Rogers speaks of trust, grumpy Senator Pastore's heart remains hardened. "Would it make you happy if you read it?" asks the senator. You can hear the patronizing swagger in his voice.

Mr. Rogers explains that for only $6,000, he can produce an episode of *Mister Rogers' Neighborhood* – less than the cost of 2 minutes of violent cartoons. And he pauses to acknowledge that he knows Senator Pastore shares his concerns about what programs kids watch on TV.

Shares his concerns? Based on Senator Pastore's demeanor, one would imagine the man eats boiled puppies for dinner. But Mr. Rogers sees something that we do not.

"I'm trying to understand the inner needs of children," Mr. Rogers continues. "We don't have to bop someone over the head to make drama...We deal with such things as getting a haircut, or the feelings about brothers and sisters and the kind of anger that arises in simple family situations. And we speak to it constructively."

Just 2 minutes into the hearing, Senator Pastore quietly asks, "How long a program is it?" You see that his posture is relaxed and open. The senator's entire persona is visibly softened. Fred Rogers has dissipated John Pastore's fierce cynicism.

After a few more minutes' testimony, Mr. Rogers concludes.

"I think it's wonderful," remarks Senator Pastore. "I think it's wonderful! Looks like you just earned your 20 million dollars."

With that, the audience laughs because they have seen an uncommonly calm, unassuming educator of small children defeat all that hostility. No, not defeat, win over through that same kindness he showed kids throughout his career.

If you loved Mr. Rogers as a child, now as a young adult and aspiring leader you ought to reconsider the man's visionary leadership and deft skill at handling conflict.

MARINE'S DISOBEDIENCE GARNERS HIM THE MEDAL OF HONOR[60]

And soon, the patrol was pinned down, taking ferocious fire from three sides. Men were being wounded and killed. Americans were surrounded. Four times, Dakota Meyer asked permission to go in; four times he was denied. It was, he was told, too dangerous.

But one of the teachers in his high school once said, "When you tell Dakota he can't do something, he's going to do it." And as Dakota said of his trapped teammates, "Those were my brothers, and I couldn't just sit back and watch."

The story of what Dakota did next will be told for generations. He told his friend Juan that they were going in. Juan jumped into a Humvee and took the wheel; Dakota climbed into the turret and manned the gun. As President Obama explained, "They were defying orders, but they were doing what they thought was right."

Defying orders. Doing what was right.

Again, the President: "You did your duty, [Sgt Dakota Meyer USMC], above and beyond, and you kept the faith with the highest traditions of the Marine Corps that you love."

Dakota Meyer's disobedience to orders was followed by a heroic act that saved thirty-six people.

DAKOTA MEYER

MORAL REASONING

"There is always a philosophy for lack of courage."
ALBERT CAMUS[61]

"Cowards can never be moral."
GHANDI[62]

"Valour and Cowardice"
Alfred Stevens

OBJECTIVE:
17.   Defend the claim that leaders must be skilled in moral reasoning.

THE LEADER AS PHILOSOPHER

Are answers to ethical questions unchanging? Or are they determined by the circumstances? This is the age-old question of objectivism* versus relativism, just one of the difficulties you confront as a leader attempting to "be the change that you want to see in the world."

Because officers play a special role in resolving problems that have ethical dimensions, they need to develop their capabilities in moral reasoning. This includes the need for each officer to study and wrestle with competing frameworks for determining right and wrong. This study can strengthen a leader's integrity. Its end result is that the leader rationally chooses an ethical framework and strives to apply it consistently.

*Note: Some authors use the term "moral absolutism" where we prefer the term "moral objectivism."

A leader who is familiar with "numerous diverse opinions on a subject does not merely parrot the arguments of others, but develops his own. He becomes a capable disputant, and modifies whatever does not seem well said."[63]

John of Salisbury

MORAL RELATIVISM

OBJECTIVE:
18.   Summarize the case for moral relativism.

Moral relativism denies that there are certain kinds of universal truths. In ethics, this means there are no universally valid moral principles.[64] Right and wrong depend on either the culture of a particular civilization at a particular moment in history, or simply on one's personal judgment.

Where does one find evidence to support moral relativism? Simply look at history. Judgments of right and wrong have varied over time. According to this line of thinking, ethics is really a matter of cultural acceptance. Perhaps this viewpoint sounds democratic. In the 21st century United States, slavery is deemed morally repugnant because every respectable person says it so; they "vote"

with their beliefs. In contrast, in early American history, a great many leaders believed slavery was a necessary institution that was somehow good for those enslaved, as well as their owners.

Other thinkers and leaders arrive at relativism not by looking at what a society pronounces as right or wrong but by looking inward. "So far, about morals," mused Ernest Hemingway, "I know only that what is moral is what you feel good after and what is immoral is what you feel bad after."[65] Put another way, the relativist claims right and wrong are matters of individual judgment based on how the behavior makes you feel. Author George Orwell illustrates how an intense feeling in his heart changed his view on the rightness of capital punishment.

> It was about forty yards to the gallows. I watched the bare brown back of the prisoner marching in front of me...And once, in spite of the men who gripped him by each shoulder, he stepped slightly aside to avoid a puddle on the path.
> It is curious, but till that moment I had never realized what it means to destroy a healthy, conscious man. When I saw the prisoner step aside to avoid the puddle, I saw the mystery, the unspeakable wrongness, of cutting a life short when it is in full tide.[66]
>
> – GEORGE ORWELL

Orwell's observations and feelings taught him something about morality. Does Orwell's experience mean that moral relativism is the best way to approach ethical situations? Not necessarily. One critic of moral relativism contends that if you really think about it, relativism is itself absolute in its rejection of absolutes.

IRONIC PERSPECTIVE:
The **"Dictatorship of Relativism"**

Relativism, that is, letting oneself be tossed here and there, carried about by every wind of doctrine, seems the only attitude that can cope with modern times. We are building a dictatorship of relativism that does not recognize anything as definitive and whose ultimate goal consists solely of one's own ego and desires.[67]
– JOSEPH RATZINGER

MORAL OBJECTIVISM

OBJECTIVE:
19.   Summarize the case for moral objectivism.

Objectivism is the belief that despite cultures disagreeing about ethics across human history, some moral principles have universal validity.[68] There is a truth independent of human opinion that makes something morally right or wrong. Under this view, for example, no one can claim the authority to destroy an innocent human being. The direct and voluntary killing of an innocent person is always gravely immoral.

It is objectivism, an appeal to some kind of immutable and crystal clear notion of right and wrong, that gives the victim the moral status to speak out against grave injustice. Confronted with the incomprehensible crime of the Holocaust, an objectivist would say

*Fine Print: Again, we use "moral objectivism" where others use "moral absolutism." Absolutism never admits any exceptions. "Killing is always wrong" is an absolutist statement. In contrast, moral objectivism allows for exceptions to be built into the description of the action. For example, "killing is wrong, except in self-defense or as a last resort to maintain peace," is an objectivist statement.

that the mass extermination of Jews was and is morally evil. There never could be a situation where the Holocaust would be justified. Don't tell me that you personally feel genocide is okay, cries the objectivist. Don't tell me that in your particular society at a particular moment in history the Holocaust can be considered moral.

The Jewish and Christian faiths offer a good example of moral objectivism. In the Torah, or Old Testament, Moses presents Israel with the Ten Commandments.[69] The faithful believe God issued these moral imperatives, and therefore they are valid to all people at all times. In modern times, the Air Force adopted Core Values that it claims are universal and timeless, thereby situating the Core Values squarely within the objectivist tradition.[70]

The problem facing objectivists is: Who or what determines right and wrong? How are we to know what the moral absolutes are? And why should notions of right and wrong bind those who reject the standard of truth they represent?

VIRTUE ETHICS

OBJECTIVE:

20. Summarize basic principles of virtue ethics.

The acorn becomes a tree. A girl, a woman. Cadets, leaders. According to Aristotle, "All things are to be understood in terms of the ends toward which they aim."[71] Philosophers use the term teleological. Everything that is conscious is goal-directed and working toward some kind of transformation. For mankind, that teleological idea is man's own happiness. Virtue leads us toward that end.

Authentic Happiness. What is happiness? According to Lucy from the comic *Peanuts*, "happiness is a warm puppy." A dollar store motivational poster says, "happiness is spending a day with friends." In virtue ethics, happiness is not merely feeling good or having a lot of fun. Rather, happiness is about fulfillment – the type of fulfillment that stays with you and doesn't evaporate. Put another way, happiness is a flourishing, the self-satisfaction you get by living up to your potential.[72] For example, what distinguishes humanity from the other animals is our capacity for reason. Therefore, we ought to develop our reason and really try to become rational beings. If we do that, we will be fulfilling our potential and flourishing as persons. We will achieve an authentic happiness that no one can take away. In virtue ethics, "happiness" is this high-minded flourishing, not a cheap and momentary sense of enjoyment.

Virtue as the Path to Happiness. What is virtue? Excellence in all its fullness, and the perfection of the soul. Virtue is the habitual disposition toward the

Always Wrong?

"The blacks are immeasurably better off here than in Africa . . . The painful discipline they are undergoing is necessary for their further instruction as a race."

Gen Robert E. Lee
making a relativist defense of slavery[73]

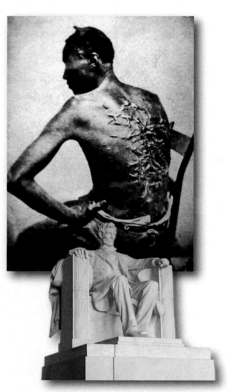

"IF SLAVERY IS NOT WRONG, NOTHING IS WRONG."
LINCOLN

making an objectivist argument against slavery[74]

teleological:
Something that is working toward a final goal or result; from the Greek *telos* for distant and *logos* for thought.

Good for its own sake.[75] Put still another way, a virtue is an excellence of your moral character that helps you become all that you can be. No wonder that the Air Force sees "excellence" as a virtue or Core Value. When someone is lazy or mediocre at his job, we object because we know he can be better. It's wrong not to do your best. It's wrong not to have a habit of striving toward goodness for its own sake. Perhaps our slacker will get into trouble at school or work and eventually disappoint everyone in his life, including himself. So the slacker's life lacks virtue and produces misery, while the focused achiever achieves virtue and becomes happy in the process. Virtue and happiness go together.

The Pursuit of Virtue. The quest for virtue is a heroic adventure and pursuit of the good life. "Men are good in one way," teaches Aristotle, "but bad in many."[76]

Right Desire. Good conduct presupposes that you have the right desire.[77] Have you ever heard of someone anonymously donating money to a charity? The donor remains secret because her desire is simply to help the charity. That desire is proper. But perhaps you've also seen someone do something nice only for the recognition. In that case, the desire is improper because it aims at recognition, not at the virtue of generosity.

True Reason. Men and women have the capability to think. Therefore, their teleological end is to be rational thinkers. You always have to be in deep thought to be virtuous because you're trying to live your life in accord with reason. The fact that people debate and philosophize and persuade one another shows that we believe good reasoning is important.[78]

Balance. Recall that in chapter 3, we discussed Aristotle's golden mean. Virtue lies between two extremes. For example, it's wrong to be a nosey neighbor. It's also wrong to be so aloof that you don't know your neighbors. It's best to be friendly with your neighbors while still respecting their privacy. This idea of balance is not just theoretical, it is something each person can discover on his or her own, through reason. A person who is inclined to shyness becomes virtuous by being a bit more outgoing and daring to accept a public speaking assignment. A person who is inclined to be an outgoing chatterbox (the opposite of our shy person) becomes virtuous by listening more carefully and acting with a bit more reserve.

Discipleship. Right and wrong is whatever produces and expresses character of a certain sort, the type of character we call virtue. In this way, each person is a disciple, a disciplined follower of an "ideal man." For example, regardless of its religious message, the "WWJD" bracelets some Christians wear ("What Would Jesus Do") illustrate the principle. These individuals are saying that they measure their actions against an idealized figure, in their case, Jesus. As such, they are pursuing virtue ethics. Likewise, Air Force lore is filled with idealized figures, paragons of virtue. Air Force Academy cadets, for example, study the steadfast loyalty and valor of Capt Lance Sijan, a

Is Lucy from Peanuts right that "happiness" is simply a warm puppy? Or is it something more?

W.W.S.D?
WHAT WOULD SIJAN DO?

Lance Sijan
The Medal of Honor recipient sets the standard for loyalty and valor. Asking, "What would Sijan do?" is a pathway toward virtue.

Medal of Honor recipient. When confronted with a physically painful obstacle, Academy cadets might draw upon Capt Sijan's heroism as inspiration, thereby propelling themselves toward virtue.

Habits of Character. Most of all, virtue is supposed to be a habit of character. Practice virtuous acts enough and you're sure to really "own" those virtues. Virtue will flow from you naturally in all you do. When the virtuous person stubs her toe, she cries "ouch!" not "fu#&a@!" Why? Because the habit of using only proper language and avoiding cuss words has taken root.

CRITICISM OF VIRTUE ETHICS

Who can argue against virtue ethics? Temperance, prudence, fortitude, and justice are all good things. Who could be against them?

One criticism is that virtue ethics simply does not square with how people live. The constant over-analysis of desire, reason, and balance is a chore. On a spectacular Friday afternoon, you feel the urge to play hooky and go do something fun. But wait, would that action be situated on the midpoint between sloth and frenzy? The question is preposterous. Critics contend that Aristotle's ethics repress young people of energy and feeling. Most of us want to live morally, but also with gusto and occasional abandon.[79]

Second, virtue ethics depends upon rational self-analysis. Many of us are poor judges of our own shortcomings. We are either too easy or too hard on ourselves. We're simply not in a position to be a truly reasonable and dispassionate observer of our own life. Consequently, it is difficult for us as individuals to find the golden mean between two extremes.

DUTY ETHICS

OBJECTIVE:
21.   Summarize basic principles of duty ethics.

Can we articulate a pure system of ethics, one built upon reason alone, not religion or personal feelings or semantics? That was the goal of Immanuel Kant.

The Concept of Duty. Kant's system of ethics begins with the concept of duty, what a person is obligated or required to do.[80] Kant reasoned that there are positive duties – I have a duty to act, a duty to yell, "Fire!" if the building starts to burn. And there are negative duties – I have a duty not to act, such as not to kill an innocent person. Along the same lines, there are perfect duties – duties that are always in

Virtue Ethics:
No Fun Allowed?

If you must constantly analyze your actions, how can you ever have fun?

effect and offer no wiggle-room or margin for personal preference. Again, the duty not to kill an innocent is a good example. And finally there is an imperfect duty, a duty to act, but with a degree of leeway or personal preference. You have a duty to honor your parents, for example, but you can go about that in many different ways.

So, if you always do your duty, you're an ethical person? Not necessarily. Kant believed duty must be fulfilled for the sake of duty. As a free person, if you act only because of your obligation, you are effectively taking refuge in slavery.[81] You'd be acting out of a desire to comply with the law or not get into trouble. In that case, your desire, not your reason, is in charge. However, the person who chooses to act for the sake of duty exercises his or her freedom and is living in accordance with reason.

The Categorical Imperative. Kant's most important contribution to ethics is his idea of the categorical imperative. "Act only on that maxim which you can at the same time will as a universal law."[82] Imagine if you were proclaimed King of the Universe. Everything you did, how you treated people, whether you lied or stole, whether you respected others or took advantage of them, became the law of the universe. Everyone had to follow your example. Kant reasoned that to discover if a course of action is moral you should simply ask, "What if everyone did this?"

The Practical Imperative. Our final Kantian point about ethics is sometimes called the practical imperative. "Act so as to treat every rational being... never as a means only, but always also as an end."[83]

People are not things. Their reason gives them dignity. In fact, it is reason that commands morality. Therefore, we ought to respect reason.

What does this mean? Don't "use" people. Sure, you can "use" a friend by borrowing her computer with her permission. Friends "use" one another all the time, while remaining friends. However, you cannot only "use" her for the computer. That's disrespectful of her dignity. That's not friendship. She would rightly feel "used" because she does not matter to you except as a means to a computer. The practical imperative also teaches that people have inalienable rights that even the majority cannot take away. As we'll see, this idea is completely opposed by utilitarianism.

CRITICISM OF DUTY ETHICS

Okay, sure, act from duty. Act as if what you do becomes the universal law. Treat everyone as an end in themselves, never use someone. On paper, those are fine ethical principles. But real life is messy. Often, one duty comes into conflict with another. What then? If

King of the World
In duty ethics, you "pretend" that your actions make the rules for the whole world.

*Fine Print:
The Categorial vs.
The Practical Imperative

A technical distinction may be helpful here. Note that the categorical imperative is a negative statement. ("Act only if..."). In other words, the categorical imperative says, "Do NOT act unless..." In contrast, the practical imperative familiar to most everyone as "the golden rule," is a positive statement. "Do unto others as you would have them do unto you."

racing a bleeding person to the hospital, is it okay to speed? To run red lights? Moreover, Kant was only half right when he said we are rational beings. We are also emotional beings. Our feelings are a very real part of what makes us human. But for Kant, emotion is not helpful in solving ethical problems. Kant's perfect world is governed by pure duty, not soft, irrational feelings or sympathies.

Stop. Go? Stop? Go!!
Duties can come into conflict with one another. Observe your duty to stop at all the red lights, or race through them in fulfilling your duty to bring your dying mother to the hospital?

UTILITARIANISM

OBJECTIVE:
22.   Summarize basic principles of utilitarian ethics.

Ethics is a matter of producing the greatest amount of happiness for the greatest number of people. That is the basis of utilitarianism, a philosophy developed by Jeremy Bentham and John Stuart Mill.

Like duty ethics, utilitarianism values human reason. We will measure happiness using reason, almost mathematically. Eating an ice cream sundae gives me 12 happiness points, for example, while taking a vacation in the mountains gives me 90 happiness points. The system is called "utilitarianism" because you measure moral goodness based on its utility, its usefulness. An act is morally right if it produces utility, if it produces pleasure.[84]

Backpacking
34 happiness pts.

An Ethic of Selflessness. The heroes we celebrate are often selfless individuals who put the group's needs ahead of their own. Lieutenant Michael Murphy was fighting in Afghanistan when his SEAL team came under heavy fire. He tried to call back to the base for help, but could not get through due to the rugged terrain. In the face of almost certain death, he fought his way into the open to gain a

Rock concert
41 happiness pts.

Happiness for Utilitarians.
In virtue ethics, we made a point of defining happiness as a fulfillment or a flourishing. We said happiness was not mere enjoyment. But the utilitarians say happiness is exactly that – enjoyment, fun, personal contentment, a subjective feeling of joy. Further, utilitarians sometimes try to rate their possible actions mathematically, as these photos show.

Go flying
58 happiness pts.

Drink & drive
- 500 happiness pts.

better position to transmit a call. The deliberate, heroic act deprived him of cover, exposing him to direct enemy fire. Finally making contact with his headquarters, Lt Murphy maintained his exposed position while providing his location and requesting help. He then continued to fight the enemy until mortally wounded.[85] Perhaps this was utilitarian ethics in action. One man heroically gave up his life so that so many more men could live.

One Life for the Whole Unit Lieutenant Michael Murphy heroically sacrificed his life in Afghanistan so that his fellow Navy SEALS could survive.

We can only try to imagine what motivated Michael Murphy's selfless actions. Perhaps his conscience as a Naval officer, sworn to protect and defend the constitution of the United States, played a role. But it's of no matter to utilitarians. They are not concerned with motives. All that matters to them is the result. One way or another, Murph saved a bunch of guys for the price of one life (his own), so mathematically speaking, happiness is maximized, and the utilitarians approve. But Murph's family and friends would tell you that the utilitarians dishonor his memory because his motives were *everything*. His motivation to be a selfless servant going above and beyond the call of duty is what made him a hero.

Justice. Utilitarianism is concerned not only with your individual happiness, but with justice, too. Mill wanted to order the world such that together we would produce the greatest happiness for the greatest number of people. What does he mean by "justice"?

"Justice implies something which is not only right to do, and wrong not to do, but which [someone] can claim from me as his moral right."[86] For example, you're a victim of a car accident. The offending driver must pay to make you whole again because that is your moral right, even though his paying you will reduce his own happiness. For justice, society will compel a person to do just acts.[87] Our courts will force a divorced parent to pay child support, for example, and will even send the offender to prison if necessary. "Only with justice and binding rules of obligation," wrote Mill, "can man achieve the greatest happiness for the greatest number."[88] Utilitarians seek justice because humankind is happier in a just society than in an unjust one.

A Leader for America's Least Powerful With enormous conviction, informed by her deep personal faith, Eunice Kennedy Shriver (second from right in this painting) labored on behalf of America's least powerful people, the mentally retarded. Her most celebrated accomplishment was her founding of the Special Olympics, an institution that is a pure reflection of objectivist ethics in championing dignity for all. Ronald Reagan presented her with the Presidential Medal of Freedom.

CRITICISM OF UTILITARIANISM

Earlier we considered the happiness point values of ice cream sundaes and mountain vacations. Who can really say ice cream is worth 12 points and not 14 or 20 or 43.875? What wins the happiness battle: poetry or new sneakers? Critics say that utilitarianism is too subjective, too prone to a biased person's faulty "guesstimates."

Moreover, this point system becomes even less reliable when the moral problem involves the happiness of several people. Utilitarianism depends upon your having a fair and honest way to quantify and weigh the happiness of everyone affected.[89]

Perhaps an even tougher criticism of utilitarianism is that it leaves us wondering how to balance the happiness of the individual against the happiness of another or of the group. A peeping Tom gets satisfaction by watching his victims, who do not experience any dissatisfaction because they do not know they are being watched. The peeping Tom supposedly creates happiness! Most people would say that's absurd. We just know that creeps are morally repugnant.

Peeping Toms
If utilitarians value personal happiness, how would they argue against peeping Toms?

Your needs and wants might conflict with the group's needs and wants. Therefore, utilitarianism must explain how far beyond the call of duty you must go to satisfy the group. Lt Murphy is undoubtedly a hero. But was he morally obligated to give up his life so that his friends would survive? Utilitarians say yes, unreservedly. One life for ten is mathematically a bargain. So much for human dignity and the belief that every person is of unique and irreplaceable value.

One thing is certain: utilitarianism may not be a perfect moral philosophy, but it does raise some troubling questions.

CONCLUSION: The MARK of an ETHICAL LEADER

Ethics encompasses so many theories because so many sincere, honest men and women have invested lifetimes of brainpower to the great conversation of moral philosophy. No one theory seems to be a silver bullet. As an aspiring young leader, you must figure out what makes one action right and another action wrong. What is your criteria? Is that criteria rational? How are you going to live in accordance with that criteria? It seems there is more to integrity than what you first learned as an airman.

The mark of an ethical leader is a willingness to take moral challenges seriously, to think deeply about a personal code of ethics, and to apply that code consistently. We return to the warning posed in this section's opening epigraph: "There is always a philosophy for lack of courage."

CAN WAR BE MORAL?

OBJECTIVE:
23. Summarize the principles of "just war theory" according to Aquinas.

"Thou shall not kill." Over one billion Christians and Jews try to live by that commandment, and billions of others try to abide by it as well. And yet human history is marked by war. Is it conceivable that war could actually be justifiable? Yes, but only under very stringent conditions, according to "Just War Theory." Summarized below are the "just war" principles of Thomas Aquinas, which have provided a moral framework for war for over 700 years.[90]

War is moral only if waged as a last resort.
Diplomacy must be given every opportunity to save the peace.

War is moral only if waged by a legitimate authority.
A democratic government wages the war, not a band of outlaws.

Al-Qaeda's attack of 9/11 was indefensible because it violated the principles of just war theory. It was an unprovoked, sneak attack by a band of stateless terrorists against civilians of a nation that would not surrender – an attack that would bring more war, not a new and lasting peace.

War is moral only if it pursues a just cause.
Those attacked must deserve it in response to their crimes; the attacked have the right of self-defense.

War is moral only if it is fought with right intentions.
Violence is permitted only to redress an injury; revenge and anger are not honorable intentions.

War is moral only if it can be fought with a reasonable chance of success.
What separates heroism from madness is the fact that the hero believes victory is possible, while the madman knows it is not.

War is moral only if its goal is to re-establish peace.
Rational individuals and nations seek justice, so to be just, warfare must produce a better and more lasting peace than the current situation.

War is moral only if the pain inflicted is proportional to the injuries suffered.
Nuclear weapons cannot be used to counter a small-scale attack.

War is moral only if every effort is made to spare the lives of the innocent non-combatants.
Hospitals and schools are not legitimate targets.

CHARACTER FORMATION

OBJECTIVE:
24. Define the term "character education."

What is character education? For our purposes, character education is any program designed to shape directly and systematically the behavior of young people. Further, character education must promote nonrelativistic values that lead to good habits and responsible citizenship.[91]

How can cadet officers help junior-ranking cadets develop character? Moreover, as indirect leaders who exert their influence through NCOs and first-line supervisors, how can cadet officers form character from afar?

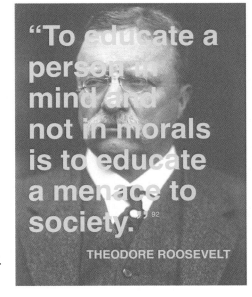

"To educate a person in mind and not in morals is to educate a menace to society."[92]

THEODORE ROOSEVELT

CHARACTER EDUCATION THROUGH BEHAVIORISM

OBJECTIVES:

25. Define the term "behaviorism."
26. Give examples of a behaviorist approach to character education.
27. Describe the strengths and weaknesses of behaviorism.

What if you had some levers that could influence your team members' character? Turn this knob, flick that switch, and perhaps your team members would know, feel, and display the sorts of values you'd like them to.

In character education, behaviorism is a belief in systematically employing rewards and punishments to control behavior.[93a] For example, students who follow the rules and aren't referred to the principal might earn the privilege of watching movies on Friday. Merit and demerit systems used at some CAP encampments are another example, at least when they try to affect individual character.

Do reward systems or merit and demerit systems really work? Many experts believe they don't. One reason is that it's easy to give demerits and concoct punishments for them, but it's difficult to find genuine reasons to award merits. After all, aren't people supposed to be staying out of trouble? Why should that earn a reward? Moreover, real life is not a reward system: you will not always win points for being honest. Therefore, it's foolish to believe that a reward system will produce virtuous people. One theorist explains:

> We want [people] not to do unethical, hurtful things because they know these things are wrong and because they can imagine how such actions will affect other people. Punishment doesn't contribute at all to the development of such concerns.[93b]

Another method of character education through behaviorism is called modeling. Through modeling, people are exposed to role models who engage in valued behaviors.[94] Much of the cadet experience is based on a belief that leadership by example, for instance, produces good and trustworthy followers. But modeling and leadership by example is not foolproof. No one is ever a perfect role model. And with youth in particular, if the role model isn't "cool," that role model will not be able to develop a strong enough rapport to be effective.

Perhaps the least effective way to do character education is sermonizing. Every teen knows how to tune out those nagging, preachy-style lectures.

Manufacturing Character
Turn the knob and out comes more character and virtue. Does the behaviorist approach have the right idea on how to build character?

Merit & Demerit Systems
The "341" used in many cadet and Air Force training environments is an example of character education through behaviorism.

Awesome Role Models
Behaviorists would tell leaders that their status as role models is their most powerful tool in developing character in others. Here, one of the most decorated Pararescuemen of all time, CMSgt Wayne Fisk, (RIGHT) encourages two cadets. Chief Fisk is a former cadet from Alaska Wing.

THE DEVELOPMENTAL PERSPECTIVE

OBJECTIVE:

28. Summarize the concept of "developmentalism" as it relates to character education.

If reward systems, role models, sermonizing, and other forms of behaviorism are imperfect, what's a better approach?

In contrast to the behaviorists, the developmentalists are concerned with how individuals systematically mature in their approach to moral and character issues over the life span. It's an appreciation for the growing capacity of independent thought.[95]

For example, the developmentalists believe that the central theme of being a teenager is the question of identity. Who am I? What do I really believe? What do I truly stand for? Every teen consciously or unconsciously tries to work these questions out.

> *Young people in their teens are faced with certain basic tasks in their growth as persons. They must find out who they are, what they believe in, and what kind of people they want to be. They must decide what kind of world they want to live in and how they are to be part of that world. Toward these ends, it is desirable that they consciously choose a set of values, interiorize them, and through choices and repeated acts strive to live in a manner consistent with those values.[96]*

Instead of rewarding and punishing people, if we want to help them develop into mature people who are choosing a set of values and striving to live up to those values, we need to be mindful of how moral development works. What stages do people pass through along their journey toward a mature moral sense?

The Key to Wisdom
Did the Ancients have it right? The oracle of Delphi put forth "know thyself" as the key to wisdom. That's close to how one developmentalist put it: "Teens . . . must find out who they are, what they believe in, and what kind of people they want to be."[97]

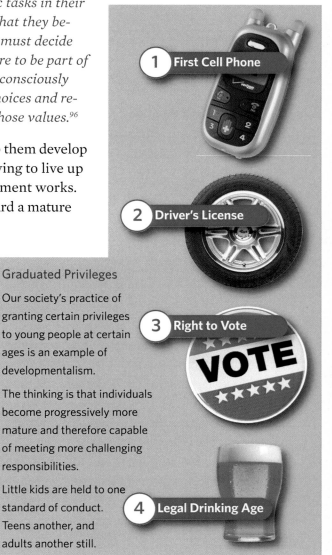

1 First Cell Phone

2 Driver's License

3 Right to Vote

4 Legal Drinking Age

FIRST THINGS

"Who am I? Why am I here?"[98] Two questions that most vice presidential candidates don't use when opening a debate.

But James B. Stockdale was no ordinary candidate.

Not understanding the significance of his rhetorical questions, many people thought Admiral Stockdale was a lost, crazy old koot, not a Stanford-educated philosopher and Medal of Honor recipient.

"Who am I? Why am I here?" Consider those profound questions. No leader can embark on a campaign before wrestling in the existential and developmental arenas.

Graduated Privileges

Our society's practice of granting certain privileges to young people at certain ages is an example of developmentalism.

The thinking is that individuals become progressively more mature and therefore capable of meeting more challenging responsibilities.

Little kids are held to one standard of conduct. Teens another, and adults another still.

KOHLBERG'S STAGES OF MORAL DEVELOPMENT

OBJECTIVES:

29. Identify the six stages in Kohlberg's theory of moral development.
30. Explain how leaders might apply Kohlberg's teachings as they try to mold the character of subordinates.
31. Describe some criticisms of Kohlberg's theory and/or developmentalism in general.

Lawrence Kohlberg found that each person passes through a series of six stages in the course of their moral development. He believed these stages are sequential; that is, you don't ever skip a step in your development. Think of Kohlberg as being like a Maslow for morals. In brief, the six stages are:[99]

Obedience and Punishment: "How can I avoid punishment?" A toddler will sit still only to avoid being punished. He or she makes no appeal to "fairness."

Individualism: "What's in it for me? What do I get for following the rules?" Children at this level struggle as they learn about sharing. There's no thought paid to the needs and feelings of other people.

Interpersonal Relations: "I want to be liked and I'm learning that means I have to treat others as I want to be treated." School-age kids and younger teens are here. This level involves the individual's attempt to conform to the group's values, or the expectations of authority figures.

The Social Order: Reasoning from a law-and-order perspective; right and wrong is a matter of rules and laws and other externals. Older teens and most adults are here. Something is right or wrong if it complies with or runs against the law.

Social Contract: Concern for individual "rights," majority rule, and democratic principles that are higher than mere written law. Individuals at this stage are willing to set aside the law, if they believe it to be unjust. They ask, "What makes a good society?"

Universal Principles: Living in accordance with conscience, regardless of external pressures; working from timeless principles of moral choice. Few, if any, individuals consistently reach this level. Kohlberg later removed this stage from his scoring manual.

Do Dogs Read Aristotle?

Chewy knows the rules. He can sit and stay until called. He knows not to eat a treat until given permission. You might argue that dogs do indeed have something like a moral intelligence. Chewy may learn some more tricks and rules, but the kind of moral intelligence he possesses will develop no further.

Brian is learning some rules. Give him your palm and he'll give you "five." His moral intelligence will grow and mature immensely. Someday he'll read sophisticated philosophies.

Because human beings naturally develop a sense for high-level moral concepts, Kohlberg argues that the right way to build character in people is to recognize this process of maturation and to help each person grow toward the next level.

"But the bell rang!"

Ralphie wants to help his pal Flick get his tongue unstuck from the icy metal pole. But how can he? The bell rang!

At Ralphie's stage of moral development, THE RULES matter most. He simply isn't aware of a higher duty to help a friend in need. The scene is Kohlberg in action.

But Ralphie's learning. Later on he allows Schwartz to skip a step when issuing the famous Triple Dog Dare.

Perhaps Ralphie's growing moral intelligence convinced his dad to buy him that official Red Ryder BB gun with a compass in the stock, and this thing which tells time.[100]

Kohlberg's Principles for Character Education. The experience gained by wrestling with moral issues is what Kohlberg believed makes people grow in wisdom. The process of discussing and debating ethical questions causes people to rethink and refine their initial and immature positions, thereby propelling them up Kohlberg's stages.[101] Therefore, leaders who want to conduct character education should challenge the weak spots of their followers' logic, or help them see other dimensions to moral issues that appear simple at first glance. Through that approach, individuals display a more mature judgment, and a more considered and reflective approach to moral issues. To clarify, Kohlberg acknowledged that right and wrong are often obvious. However, his system recognizes that in adult life, moral difficulties are complex, and therefore a mature reasoning will perceive the complicated intersections formed when multiple virtues and multiple vices collide.

How Leaders Apply Kohlberg. No lectures, no sermons. No manipulations, no contrived merits or demerits. Instead, leaders try to assist their followers or students in reaching the next stage of their moral development. As mentioned above, this is largely a matter of Socratic discussion. In group settings, the goal is not for everyone to arrive at the same "answer," but to engage in some mental gymnastics as they wrestle with the issues and think deeply about them.

Criticism of Kohlberg's Theory. Have you ever met someone who talks a good game, but in real life has no actual integrity? At least one critic believes Kohlberg's stages measure intellectual development, not a person's actual commitment to Core Values. "Kohlberg's scale has to do with moral thinking, not moral action...People who can talk at a high moral level may not behave accordingly."[102]

PRACTICAL WAYS TO APPLY KOHLBERG'S DEVELOPMENTALISM

- Challenge your followers' or students' assumptions

- Ask your follower to explain the situation from another person's perspective

- Make your follower predict likely outcomes

- Have your follower identify the rights, virtues, and goods at stake

- Have your follower identify the vices, temptations, treachery that might come into play

- Modify the problem or situation by asking "What if...?"

- Ask your follower to identify the weakest link in their own argument

- Examine the precedents; has a similar issue come up before and how was it handled?

- Go beyond the rules or the laws. Will those rules and laws, even if enforced perfectly, reflect our ideals of fairness?

The Military Perspective. Is Kohlberg just something kindergarten teachers worry about as they teach little kids to share? Hardly. His theory of moral development closely follows the perspective of one noted author and retired Air Force general:

> *Ethical decisions become ever more complex as individuals grow in power, prestige, and rank. Good moral values will sometimes be in conflict. You must apply ethics with wisdom and maturity. This may be the greatest challenge and the greatest opportunity for the enlightened leader.*[103]

CONFLICT RESOLUTION

OBJECTIVES:

32. Define the term "conflict," in the context of "interpersonal conflict."
33. Defend the claim that leaders must possess good conflict resolution skills.

In everything human, conflict is inevitable. This fact is obvious to most everyone. And yet, people typically do not study interpersonal conflict in a serious manner. So many otherwise responsible adults are unaware how to reconcile incompatible thoughts and behaviors between themselves and others.[104]

How severe is this problem? One researcher found that "even when it comes to important issues, people only recall about 35% of what they [discussed] the previous hour."[105] In other words, most people lack conflict management skills and tend to get so wrapped up in their particular conflicts that they aren't entirely sure what they are saying.

Leaders, therefore, face a challenge. Leaders are expected not only to be proficient in managing the conflicts that arise in their lives, but in helping others manage conflict as well. If you wish to lead, you will need to acquire special expertise in resolving conflict.

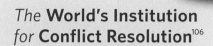

The **World's Institution** *for* **Conflict Resolution**[106]

"WE THE PEOPLES
OF THE
UNITED NATIONS
DETERMINED

to save succeeding generations from the scourge of war. . .

to reaffirm faith in fundamental human rights. . .

to establish conditions under which justice and. . .international law can be maintained. . .

to unite our strength to maintain international peace and security. . .

do hereby establish an international organization to be known as the United Nations."

SIGNED IN SAN FRANCISCO IN 1945 BY

CHINA

FRANCE

UNION OF SOVIET SOCIALIST REPUBLICS

UNITED KINGDOM OF GREAT BRITAIN AND NORTHERN IRELAND

UNITED STATES OF AMERICA

FIVE TYPES OF CONFLICT

OBJECTIVE:

34.   Describe each of the five types of conflict.

To reduce or resolve conflict, first we need to understand it. What does conflict look like? In what kinds of shapes, sizes, or flavors is it found? For our purposes, we will consider five types of conflict.[107, 108]

Parallel Conflict has an objective basis. That is, the matter upon which the parties disagree is a real thing. Moreover, the two (or more) disagreeing parties accurately perceive what is in conflict. This shared understanding of the conflict is why it is called "parallel." If mom asks what two kids want for lunch, perhaps the boy wants a warm bowl of beef stew because it's cold outside, while the girl wants to keep it light and just have a salad. Each understands the other's position. The conflict is clear, but unresolved, and is said to be parallel.

Displaced Conflict also has an objective basis. (Again, the conflict is "real" and "verifiable.") In these situations, there is the true, underlying conflict, but attention is paid to the manifest or apparent conflict. More simply, in a displaced conflict, people argue about the wrong thing. Suppose you are developing a steady relationship that your mom disapproves of. Your mom begins to complain that by spending too much time at the mall, your grades are suffering. In response, you argue about grades, time at the mall, whether you get your homework done, etc. All the while, the real issue is your mom is unhappy that you hang out at the mall with your potential boyfriend or girlfriend, but that conflict is not addressed. The conflict is displaced.

Misattributed Conflict happens when the conflict is inaccurately perceived such that it is attributed to the wrong person. Perhaps one of the parties is simply confused about what's at issue, or perhaps someone is manipulating events behind-the-scenes to deliberately cloud their judgment. Consider a trio of friends, Amanda, Becci, and Cherry, for instance. For some reason, Amanda becomes jealous of the others, so to "get even" she whispers hurtful things to each, making Becci think Cherry hates her (Becci), and vice versa. Becci and Cherry will come into conflict, each believing she has a gripe against the other. In fact they should be mad at Amanda, but they don't realize that. The conflict is misattributed.

A poet wonders about the roots of conflict . . .

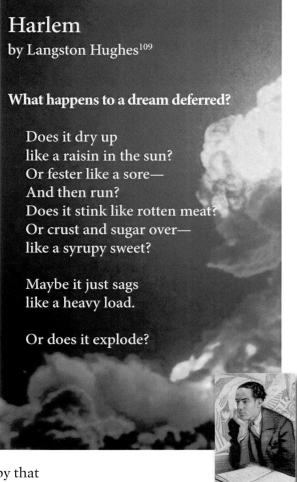

Harlem
by Langston Hughes[109]

What happens to a dream deferred?

Does it dry up
like a raisin in the sun?
Or fester like a sore—
And then run?
Does it stink like rotten meat?
Or crust and sugar over—
like a syrupy sweet?

Maybe it just sags
like a heavy load.

Or does it explode?

Note: Recall that we define conflict as a disagreement through which individuals perceive a threat to their needs, interests, or concerns.[110] In chapter 6, we introduced the concept of interpersonal conflict. In this chapter we take a deeper look into the field.

Latent Conflict is that which should be occurring, but is not. Do you like dealing with conflict? Lots of people don't. In fact, many of us avoid conflict if at all possible. Latent conflicts may go away on their own, continue for years, or eventually explode. Suppose a new, energetic senior member has not quite learned how to relate to the cadet staff. He monopolizes classroom discussions and interrupts you when you are training junior-ranking cadets. You hate this. But confronting an authority figure is so unpleasant, you decide to suffer in silence. In turn, the senior member's domineering style continues for weeks. The conflict is real, but you are keeping it under wraps. The conflict is latent.

False Conflict is the tragic case of disagreements that have no basis in reality. Surely you've been mad about something, only to find out that your anger was not justified. Misunderstandings produce false conflicts. Suppose an officer were to advocate that cadet training include anti-bullying, equal opportunity, and anti-discrimination topics. Another leader objects, insisting that cadets be trained in Core Values. Although they do not realize it, both parties want the same thing. Their use of jargon is causing confusion. After all, the Core Value of "Respect" suggests that bullying, discrimination, and the like are simply not tolerated. In truth, there is no disagreement here. This is a false conflict.

Suffering in Silence
Conflict can be so unpleasant that many of us will avoid it at all costs. When a conflict should be occurring but is not, the situation is said to exhibit latent conflict.

LESSON FOR CADET OFFICERS

Some conflicts reflect real problems, while others reflect perceived problems. Sometimes one party is misguided, sometimes both. Because there is no single type of conflict, there is no single approach or solution to conflict. The successful leader must be adaptable and carry a mixed bag of tools for resolving conflict.

A MODEL OF INTERPERSONAL CONFLICT

OBJECTIVES:
35.   Describe what occurs during each of the five phases of the model of interpersonal conflict.
36.   Describe some of the key points for managing conflict effectively.

What's really going on inside an interpersonal conflict? If we try to look at interpersonal conflict scientifically, what do we observe? So far we've discussed the important role leaders play in resolving conflict, and five different types of conflict. Next we'll consider a model that explains the contexts, interactions, and outcomes that are found in interpersonal conflict. [111]

Distal (Background) Context.   There's always a context to a conflict, a setting or a history that shapes the conflict from the beginning. The

This section studies the anatomy of conflicts. For tips on mediating conflict, see chapter 6.

people involved in the conflict carry these circumstances into the conflict event. Imagine that you have surpassed the cadet who recruited you and now you outrank him. If you preside over his next promotion board, there might be some animosity. He used to know lots more about CAP than you, but now you're the superior and he's the subordinate. These circumstances set the stage for the event and provide context.

Some sources of distal context include national culture, family situation, individual personality and experiences, history of the communicators' relationship with one another, and the maturity and wisdom of the communicators.

Leaders need to be aware that a distal context can be shaping an interpersonal conflict. They should be mindful of how past events and memories of conflicts from of old can shape the conflicts of today.

Proximal (Immediate) Context. If you have a long history with someone — a sibling or best friend, for example — your relationship will have a rich distal context. But your proximal or immediate context is more pressing on the conflict you're faced with today.   Proximal context refers to the immediate circumstances affecting the conflict. It includes the communicator's goals — "I want to win this fight over what we'll watch on TV" — and the emotions that come into play. Proximal conflict also includes the cause-and-effect of the conflict, the communicator's sense of what is causing the problem and what effect it is having on people.

"Perception is reality" is an old saying that describes proximal context. A communicator brings to the conflict his or her perceptions about its immediate context. Those perceptions may be terribly mistaken and heated by strong emotions, but they are real, at least in one person's perspective.

**Top 10 Conflict Areas
Between Teens and Parents**[112]

Fighting with siblings
Doing homework
Getting up in the morning
Cleaning the bedroom
Putting clothes away
Eating habits
Helping out around the house
Talking back to a parent
Going to bed on time
Turning off the lights

· ·

Noteworthy by their absence:

Drugs, alcohol, and tobacco
Dating and sex
Choice of friends
Getting in trouble at school
Clothing choices

Model of a Conflict Episode

CONTEXTS			OUTCOMES	
Distal Context	**Proximal Context**	**Conflict Interaction**	**Proximal Outcomes**	**Distal Outcomes**
The immediate circumstances that affect the conflict.	The long-term history framing the conflict.	The give-and-take of the conflict itself, including the message tactics and strategies employed.	Initial thoughts and feelings about the conflict; its immediate results.	Long-range results of the conflict. Today's distal outcomes form tomorrow's distal context when the next conflict arises.

Adapted from William R. Cupach, et al., Competence in Interpersonal Conflict, 2d ed., (Long Grove, IL: Waveland Press, 2010).

Leaders should remember that good leadership is thoughtful, not a "seat of your pants" endeavor. The proximal context will affect how the conflict will unfold. Therefore, it's important to remember that knee-jerk, shoot-first/ask questions later attitudes will spin a conflict into further chaos.

Conflict Interaction. Welcome to the event. The conflict interaction is the focal process of the conflict, the moment when the two or more communicators butt heads. While distal and proximal context are often only partially visible, the conflict interaction is the conflict's most visible feature. During these moments of give-and-take, the communicators deploy their message tactics and strategies to "win" the conflict. The element of surprise has a part to play, too. The tactics and strategies that the other person deploys causes you to react, and the unexpected can spin the conflict into surprising directions.

Proximal Outcomes. Immediately following the conflict, we see the proximal outcomes, the immediate outcomes. During this phase, the communicators take stock in what just happened. They sort through their thoughts and feelings. Did I "win"? Did I achieve what I wanted? These initial thoughts and feelings shape the communicator's opinions about the conflict episode. Of course, those opinions may or may not agree with reality. Emotions might still be running high.

But not all conflict is loaded with emotions, ready to explode. If a communicator feels that the other side listened well and behaved responsibly, the proximal outcome will be at least somewhat positive. People appreciate having their voices heard. We all want to "have our day in court."

Leaders should know that how we feel immediately after a conflict episode will change. It'll look different tomorrow. Proximal outcomes are not the end of the story.

Leaders & Distal Outcomes
A single conflict episode may have a lasting effect. How well leaders respond to attempts at peaceful interpersonal conflict can determine if the distal outcome – the long-term future – is peaceful or escalates into violence.

Distal Outcomes. A single conflict episode may have a lasting effect. The conflict's effects might slowly emerge as time goes by and the thoughts, feelings, and practical results of the conflict settle down. These distal outcomes concern the long-term maintenance or deterioration of the various individuals' relationships.

What becomes of distal outcomes? Today's distal outcomes form tomorrow's distal context. The old saying, "don't burn your bridges" illustrates the importance of distal, not just proximal, outcomes.

Leaders think long-term. Know that it is shortsighted to try to "win" every conflict no matter what the cost. The concept of distal outcomes should remind wise leaders that how they resolve conflicts today can build good relationships tomorrow, or make it impossible to work effectively with others in the future.

KEY POINTS FOR MANAGING CONFLICT[113]

How conflict is managed can lead to the creation (or not) and maintenance of relationships that provide for better coordination and responsiveness. Effective conflict management involves the following steps:

1. Describe what you see through factual observation.

2. Explore and consider the universe of interpretations to the event/behavior.

3. Map the dimensions of the conflict, participants, and process.

4. Evaluate your interpretation and identify if there are positive and negative reactions to the event/behavior.

5. Analyze the causes of the conflict in light of:
   • Relationship Issues – the "who" of the disagreement.
   • Substantive Issues – the "what" of the disagreement.
   • Procedural Issues – the "how" of the disagreement.

6. Allow each party to voice her perspective and experience, which validates each party's worth and right to be part of the discussion.

7. Reframe a fuller definition of the problem based on an understanding of multiple perspectives.

8. Develop a constructive strategy for dealing with the conflict, via:
   • Developing a collaborative planning process.
   • Building constructive working relationships.

9. Develop a range of alternative approaches or solutions and collectively test them for viability.

10. Achieve solutions that take into account interests, not positions.

Weak Leaders & Conflict
Is it any wonder that the Civil War erupted? The three presidents who preceded Lincoln are regarded as among our least effective leaders. If you can't manage conflict, get ready for the conflict to grow worse.

(13) Fillmore

(14) Pierce

(15) Buchanan

COOPERATIVE NEGOTIATION[114]

OBJECTIVES:
37. Define the term "negotiation."
38. Summarize the leader/negotiator's role.

Negotiation is a deliberate process for two or more people or groups to solve a difference or problem.[115] We have discussed interpersonal conflicts. Next we'll consider negotiation as a way to resolve conflict. Through negotiation, the parties strive to reach agreement on issues or courses of action where there is some degree of difference in interest, goals, values, or beliefs. The job of the negotiator is to build credibility with the "other side," find some common ground or shared interests, learn the opposing position, and share information that will persuade the "other side" to agree to an outcome.[116]

The majority of this section on negotiation (pp. 45-49) is excerpted from Dr. Stef Eisen, "Shortcuts to Cooperative Negotiating Strategies," Air Force Negotiation Center of Excellence, 2011, used with permission.

NEGOTIATION PREFERENCES & STYLES CHART

This chart illustrates how the five main negotiation styles compare with one another in terms of their "task orientation" (the emphasis on coming to an agreement), and the "people orientation" (the emphasis on building a good relationship).

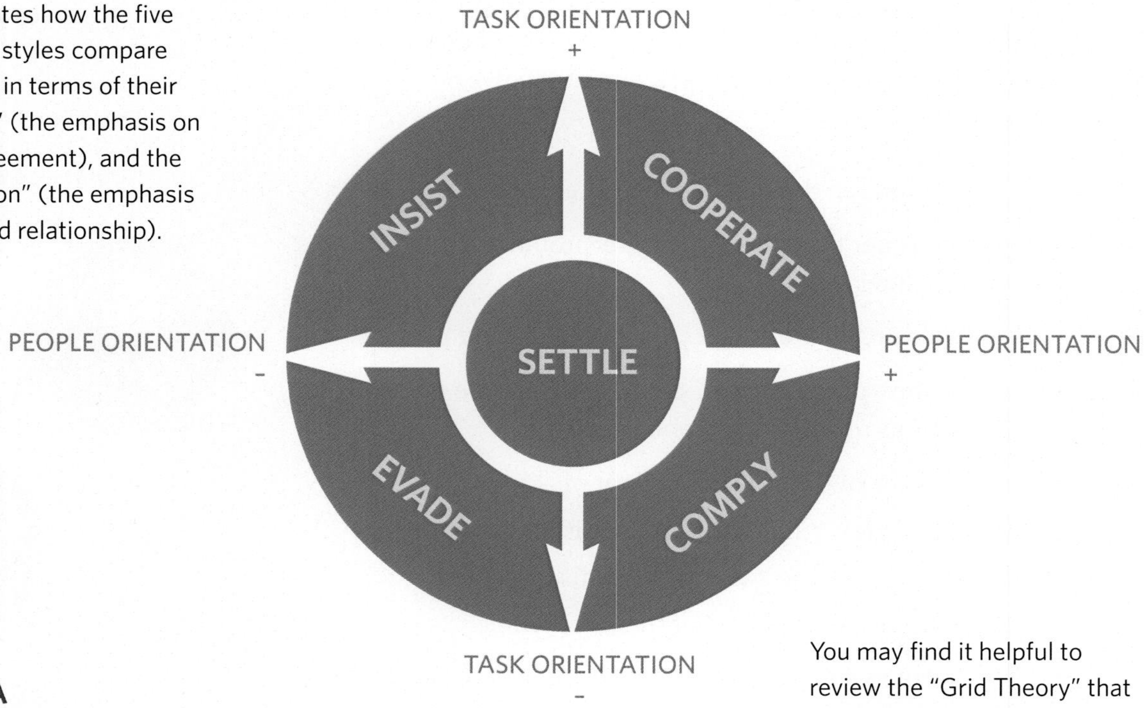

TASK ORIENTATION
+

INSIST

COOPERATE

PEOPLE ORIENTATION
−

SETTLE

PEOPLE ORIENTATION
+

EVADE

COMPLY

TASK ORIENTATION
−

You may find it helpful to review the "Grid Theory" that you studied in chapter 7, because this chart includes the same "task orientation" and "people orientation" axes.

BATNA

OBJECTIVE:
39.   Define the term "BATNA."
40.   Explain why BATNA is a significant element in the negotiation process.

If you only have time to do one thing in preparing to negotiate, always know your Best Alternative to a Negotiated Agreement (BATNA) and protect it. Simply stated, the BATNA is what you would do if negotiation would fail. If the other side insists on an idea that is less than your BATNA, there is no point in your continuing to negotiate. Likewise, always estimate the opposition's BATNA and find ways to influence it. Your BATNA can often be used to motivate the opposite party to stay in a negotiation. You can often convince the opposition to engage further in the negotiation when you reveal that you'd hate to go back to your boss and admit failure – and ask him how his boss would react upon hearing the same news.

FIVE BASIC STRATEGIES

OBJECTIVE:
41.   Describe each of the five basic negotiation strategies.
42.   Defend the claim that negotiating skills are important to leaders and cadet officers in particular.

1. Evade Strategy: The Evade strategy is a passive, unassertive strategy where you don't have any motivation to work your expectations or meet their expectations. When might you "evade" or "kick the can down the road"? Perhaps if the issue at hand is totally unimportant to you, you have higher priorities, or you lack the energy and drive to tackle the problem. Often the status quo is actually preferred to any envisioned solution. Also, you may use the Evade strategy if you are faced with an overwhelmingly competitive opponent and this forestalls an outcome that would definitely not satisfy your needs.

Evade may be useful when trust is low, you have no need for information beyond what you have, you have the power to resist the opposition's strategy, and the option of the status quo is the preferred option for you.

2. Comply Strategy: The Comply strategy tends to delegate the responsibility for the conflict's resolution with the other person or party. This (along with the "Evade" strategy) is a passive approach to negotiations. This strategy is preferred when preserving the relationship between you and the other party is the paramount concern, even if it is at the "expense of the task." The result of this strategy is that the more assertive party gets what they want and you, as the compliant side, give up whatever is at stake or grant a concession to the opposition.

Evade may be useful when trust is low to moderate, you have no need for information beyond what you have, you do not have the power to resist the opposition's strategy, and the option of giving in to the other side's interests may create a favorable situation for the next engagement with your opposition.

3. Insist Strategy: The Insist strategy is useful when you believe that obtaining your objective is paramount, regardless of the cost to the opposition's interests or the relationship. The Insist strategy is usually associated with a position and declared with a demand that leaves little room for movement and/or compromise. Information is usually hoarded and withheld. Relationships are usually put at risk and any long-term negotiating relationships are difficult to maintain. This style is preferred when a "winner takes all" requirement is sought.

Usually the Insist strategy is used when there is a single issue (like price or security), and the likelihood of further interaction between the parties is unlikely or winner's residual power after the negotiations will allow for more use of the Insist strategy. The Insist strategy is quick, and there's usually one outcome: one party "wins" and the other "loses." (Recall the "zero sum game" from chapter 6.) At issue is which party gets to play the victor or the vanquished. Usually, the party with the greater amount of power is the victor.

If the five negotiation strategies had their own bumper stickers:

The **SETTLE STRATEGY** bumper sticker

The **COMPLY STRATEGY** bumper sticker

The **INSIST STRATEGY** bumper sticker

The **EVADE STRATEGY** bumper sticker

The **COOPERATIVE STRATEGY** bumper sticker

Some suggest this winner-take-all approach is a misunderstanding of negotiations. It is not a misunderstanding, but a specific strategy available to achieve specific goals. The value of this strategy lies in appropriately selecting it to meet the conditions. Because it is short-sighted and does not consider relationships, etc., once the confrontation is won, the opposition is not likely to deal with you again. Perhaps they will not be willing to execute the plan, or will generally be a troublesome partner. The Insist strategy perhaps requires the most careful monitoring of the post-agreement compliance.

Insist may be useful when trust is low, you have no need for information beyond what you have, you have the power to overcome the opposite's strategy, and the only option you will consider is your option.

4. Settle Strategy: The Settle strategy may be useful when you seek resolution to a situation, but see little chance for you to really get it "your way" (e.g., the Insist Strategy), or you don't want to "give in" (e.g., the Comply Strategy) to the opposition.

By using the Settle strategy, you may minimally satisfy both side's task interests through the process of splitting whatever difference is separating you from the opposition, usually in the form of splitting the difference "somewhere down the middle." The Settle strategy usually opens not with a demand (a hard position with no wiggle room), but a softer "offer" (a position leaving some room for you or the opposite to maneuver the other to a solution). Each party "gets something," but usually not what you really need or what fully satisfies you. Additionally, the people orientation is not strong, as you expect the opposition to take care of their interests as you are taking care of yours. It is not antagonistic; neither is it nurturing.

Settling usually results in a quick negotiation (Settle is an efficient process), but rarely an optimal outcome (Settle is usually not an effective process). Also, the Settle strategy is usually most useful where only one variable is at stake or being considered (like price). A quick tutorial on the Settle strategy is available in any segment of *Pawn Stars* or *American Pickers* series on cable television.

Settle may be useful when trust is low to moderate; you have most of the information you need, but not all to conclude the deal; you have about equal power with your opposite; and you are willing to give a little on your desired option to close the deal.

5. Cooperative Negotiating Strategy: CNS is the Air Force Negotiation Center of Excellence's enhanced version of the business world concept known as Interest-Based Negotiations.

The Warrior / Negotiator
When US troops operate in a coalition with other nations, commanders have to convince (not order) coalition partners to operate in a way that is consistent with U.S. strategy, or vice versa. The Air Force asserts that today "warrior / negotiator" is no longer an oxymoron. Negotiation skills are becoming a larger part of professional military education.

Negotiation TV
Everyone gets something with the "Settle" strategy because you and the opposition basically split your differences down the middle. Two TV programs – *Pawn Stars* and *American Pickers* – offer good examples of Settle in action.

CNS depends on each party's desire to achieve both a mutually satisfactory outcome while simultaneously managing the relationship. For this to occur, trust must exist between the parties and they must be willing to share information and decision-making power and suspend judgment on possible solutions. The AF NCE also suggests that all five negotiation strategies discussed in this section are "interest-based" and none should be disregarded when contemplating a negotiation. For example, in certain situations your "interests" must predominate (such as using the Insist strategy in a crisis). In other situations, your interest may be for the opposite to "have it their way" (using the Comply strategy to build a relationship).

CNS, however, has the potential to address multiple issues within a negotiation. The basic premise is that the "game" is not inherently zero-sum, as in the Insist strategy, but there is a potential to create new value for each party involved while building an enduring relationship to handle the inevitable problems that crop up while executing nearly every negotiated agreement. CNS is particularly effective in a diverse situation, such as the military environment. Agreements in the military must be reached with people and groups that are often very different — culturally, socially, politically, etc. To get beyond the obstacles to an agreement, CNS suggests focusing on the underlying, basic, and perhaps common interests behind each party's initial positions. From these interests arises the potential to also find common ground and generate opportunities to create new value. Reduced to its essentials, CNS proposes that two groups working together will come up with a solution qualitatively better than what either party could generate on its own.

CNS may be useful when trust is moderate to high, you know you do not have the information you need, you have about equal power with the opposition, and you are willing to consider many options that might meet your interests as well as your opposition's interests.

IMPLICATION FOR CADET OFFICERS

Negotiation is an aspect of leadership. Both are matters of influence, involve goal-setting, and require collaboration. Cadet officers will find the need to negotiate as they cooperate with senior members in leading their units, try to resolve disputes among cadets, obtain favorable pay and time-off conditions with potential employers, work with college officials on financial aid packages, and more. In business and in life, "You don't get what you deserve, you get what you negotiate."[117]

"In business and in life, you don't get what you deserve, you get what you negotiate."

Key Questions to Ask When Preparing for Negotiation[118]

- What pre-assessment has been done before getting together?
- What are the existing relationships between the parties?
- What is the history of the issues?
- What is the collaboration history and style of the parties and the organizations they represent?
- What are the represented organizations' approaches to negotiation?
- What issues are likely to be raised within the process?

Representation

- Who are the parties, the representatives, and the decision-makers?
- Can the right people be brought to the table?
- What is the best way to convene the parties?

Mandates and Influences

- What are the institutional constraints of each party?
- Do the parties have the authority to negotiate and make decisions?
- What are the political constraints of each party?
- What are the general and specific mandates of participating agencies and others and how might they conflict?

Resources

- How will the negotiation be financed?
- Who is the lead on financing and developing the budget?
- What time and personnel investments are required?

Management

- Who will manage the process?
- How will communication be managed?
- How will the group make decisions?
- How will coalition dynamics be managed?

Note that these questions should also be revisited when the group comes together.

SPEAK UP!
Six Steps to Speaking Up Against Everyday Bigotry[119]

OBJECTIVES:

43. Identify the six practical steps for speaking up against everyday bigotry.
44. Defend the claim that leaders should not allow bigotry to go unchallenged.

Whatever situation you're in, remember these six steps to help you speak up against everyday bigotry. In any situation, however, assess your safety, both physical and emotional. There is a risk, and that must be acknowledged as you make your own choice to speak up.

This section is excerpted from "Speak Up!" by Teaching Tolerance, tolerance.org. Used with permission.

BE READY

You know another moment like this will happen, so prepare yourself for it. Think of yourself as the one who will speak up. Promise yourself not to remain silent.

"Summon your courage, whatever it takes to get that courage, wherever that source of courage is for you," said Dr. Marsha Houston, of the University of Alabama.

To bolster that courage, have something to say in mind before an incident happens. Open-ended questions often are a good response. "Why do you say that?" "How did you develop that belief?"

IDENTIFY THE BEHAVIOR

Sometimes, pointing out the behavior candidly helps someone hear what they're really saying: "Janice, what I hear you saying is that all husbands are lazy" (or whatever the slur happens to be). Or, "Janice, you're classifying an entire ethnicity in a derogatory way. Is that what I hear you saying?"

When identifying behavior, however, avoid labeling, name-calling or the use of loaded terms. Describe the behavior; don't label the person.

"If your goal is to communicate, loaded terms get you nowhere," said Dr. K.E. Supriya, an expert in the role of gender and cultural identity in communication. "If you simply call someone a racist, a wall goes up."

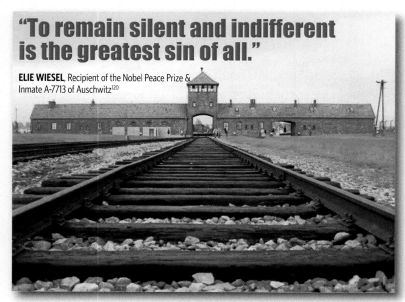

"To remain silent and indifferent is the greatest sin of all."

ELIE WIESEL, Recipient of the Nobel Peace Prize & Inmate A-7713 of Auschwitz[120]

APPEAL TO PRINCIPLES

If the speaker is someone you have a relationship with — a sister, friend or coworker, for example — call on their higher principles: "Bob, I've always thought of you as a fair-minded person, so it shocks me when I hear you say something that sounds so bigoted."

"Appeal to their better instincts," Houston said. "Remember that people are complex. What they say in one moment is not necessarily an indication of everything they think."

SET LIMITS

You cannot control another person, but you can say, "Don't tell racist jokes in my presence anymore. If you do, I will leave." Or, "My workspace is not a place I allow bigoted remarks to be made. I can't control what you say outside of this space, but here I ask that you respect my wishes." Then follow through.

"The point is to draw a line, to say, 'I don't want you to use that language when I'm around,' " Bob Carolla, spokesman for the National Alliance for the Mentally Ill. "Even if attitudes don't change, by shutting off bad behavior, you are limiting its contagion. Fewer people hear it or experience it."

FIND AN ALLY / BE AN ALLY

When frustrated in your own campaign against everyday bigotry, seek out like-minded people and ask them to support you in whatever ways they can. And don't forget to return the favor: If you aren't the first voice to speak up against everyday bigotry, be the next voice.

"Always speak up, and never be silenced out of fear," said Shane Windmeyer, founder and coordinator of Campus PrideNet and the Lambda 10 Project. "To be an ally, we must lead by example and inspire others to do the same."

BE VIGILANT

Remember: Change happens slowly. People typically make small steps, not large ones. Stay prepared, and keep speaking up. Don't risk silence.

"There's a sense of personal disappointment in having not said something when you felt you should have," said Ron Schlittler, acting executive director of the national office of Parents, Families and Friends of Lesbians and Gays.

Carolla put it this way: "If you don't speak up, you're surrendering part of yourself. You're letting bigotry win."

I PLEDGE TO SPEAK UP!

In pledging to respond to everyday bigotry, I will:

Speak up when I hear or see bigotry;

Question and identify bias when I see it;

Be mindful of my own behaviors;

Promote and appeal to higher principles;

Set limits on what is said or done around me;

Seek help and help others to work against bigotry;

Remain vigilant and persistent.

CONCLUSION

During this chapter entitled "The Cadet Officer," we have considered four main topics: officership, moral reasoning, character formation, and conflict resolution. At first glance, these topics may appear to be a hodgepodge. But upon reflection, you should recognize that the common theme is integrity.

Officers place integrity at the forefront of their concept of officership. Officers study integrity in depth to increase their capacity for moral reasoning. Officers develop integrity in others through character formation. And officers apply integrity in their attempts to resolve conflicts. Being an officer is a challenging vocation, but a rewarding one, too.

NOTES

[1] Samuel P. Huntington, *The Soldier & The State* (Cambridge MA: Harvard University Press, 1985 ed.), 28.

[2] Quoted in ibid., 30.

[3] US Air Force, AFDD 1-1, *Leadership & Force Development* (Maxwell AFB, AL, 2006), vi.

[4] *Constitution of the United States of America*, Article II, Section 3.

[5] Executive Order 10631, *Code of Conduct for Members of the Armed Forces of the United States*, as amended, 1988.

[6] Department of Defense, DD Form 1, *Officer's Commission*, 2000.

[7] U.S. Air Force, AU-24, *Concepts for Air Force Leadership* (Maxwell AFB, AL: Air University Press, 1996), 5-6.

[8] Office of the Undersecretary of Defense for Personnel & Readiness, *Population Representation in the Military Services*, Fiscal Year 2009.

[9] Author's interview with the AFROTC vice commander, December 2010.

[10] U.S. Air Force ROTC, "High School Scholarships," http://afrotc.com/scholarships/high-school/eligibility/ (accessed Feb 2011).

[11] Secretary of Defense Melvin Laird speaking at the Armed Forces Staff College in 1969, quoted in *USAF Air Command & Staff College* (Maxwell AFB, AL: Air University, 2011), chapter 1, unit 5.

[12] Stephen E. Ambrose, *D-Day: The Climactic Battle of World War II* (New York: Touchstone, 1995), 22-24. Reprinted with permission.

[13] US Army, AFM 7-22.7, *The Army Noncommissioned Officer Guide* (US Army, 2002), 1-32.

[14] Francis J. Yammarino, "Indirect Leadership: Transformational Leadership" in *Improving Organizational Effectiveness Through Transformational Leadership*, Bernard Bass & Bruce Avolio, eds. (Thousand Oaks, CA: SAGE Publications, 1994), 27.

[15] Gerry Larsson et al., "Indirect Leadership in a Military Context," in the *Leadership & Organization Development Journal*, vol. 26, no. 3, (Dec 2004): 215.

[16] Ibid., 222.

[17] Ibid., 224.

[18] Ibid., 224.

[19] Howard Gardner, *Leading Minds* (New York: Basic Books, 1995), 293.

[20] Cage Innoye, "Indirect Leadership," at http://diversephilosophy.blogspot.com (accessed Feb 2011).

[21] Yammarino, 40.

[22] Ibid., 40.

[23] Ibid., 30.

[24] Ibid., 44.

[25] Identityworks.com, Tony Spaeth, ed., "US Air Force: A use of identity, by a leader," http:www.identityworks.com/reviews/2000/usaf.htm (accessed Feb 2011).

[26] The Smoking Gun, "Van Halen's Legendary M&Ms Rider,"http://www.thesmokinggun.com/documents/crime/van-halens-legendary-mms-rider (accessed Feb 2011).

[27] Mallen Baker, "Definitions of Corporate Social Responsibility," http://www.mallenbaker.net/csr/definition.php (accessed Feb 2011).

[28] Business for Social Responsibility, quoted in Baker.

[29] Transparency International, "Frequently Asked Questions About Corruption," http://transparency.org/news_room/faq/corruption_faq#faqcorr9 (accessed Feb 2011).

[30] International Society of Sustainability Professionals, "Press Kit," http://www.sustainabilityprofessionals.org/press-kit (accessed Feb 2011).

[31] Subaru, "Subaru and the Environment," http://www.subaru.com/company/environmental-policy.html (accessed Feb 2011).

[32]

[33] Lynne Duke, "The Man Who Made Kathie Lee Cry," *Washington Post*, July 31, 2005.

[34] Louis Brandeis, "Other People's Money," *Harper's Weekly*, December 20, 1913.

[35] Transparency International.

[36] Judith Rehak, "Tylenol Made a Hero of Johnson & Johnson," *The New York Times*, March 23, 2002.

[37] John Hansen, "Before You Lay Down the Law...," *Associations Now*, American Society of Association Executives, November 2007.

[38] Monroe Edwin Price, *The V-Chip Debate* (New York: Psychology Press, 1998), 195.

[39] Hansen.

[40] Editors' Statment, "Correcting the Record; Times Reporter Who Resigned Leaves Long Trail of Deception," *New York Times*, May 11, 2003.

[41] David D. Kirkpatrick, "Historian Says Borrowing Was Wider Than Known," *New York Times*, Feb 23, 2002.

[42] Maria Newman, "Marion Jones," Times Topics, *New York Times*, Nov 30, 2009 ed.

[43] *New York Times*, "Joe Wilson," Times Topics, Sept 16, 2009 ed.

[44] Air Line Pilots Association, "Code of Ethics," http://www.alpa.org/Home/WhoWeAre/CodeofEthics/tabid/2262/Default.aspx (accessed Feb 2011).

[45] National Society of Professional Engineers, "Code of Ethics," http://www.nspe.org/Ethics/CodeofEthics/index.html (accessed Feb 2011).

[46] The Professional Aviation Maintenance Association, "AMT Code of Ethics," http://www.pama.org/about-pama/amt-code-ethics (accessed Feb 2011).

[47] Matthew L. Wald, "Was Flight 1549's Pilot Fearful? If So, His Voice Didn't Let On," *The New York Times*, http://www.nytimes.com/2009/02/06/nyregion/06crash.html (accessed Feb 2011). Web version includes ATC audio.

[48] Peter Senge, *The Fifth Discipline* (New York: Currency Doubleday, 2006 ed.), 17.

[49] Senge, 24.

[50] Leslie A. Perlow, "When Silence Spells Trouble at Work," *Harvard Business Review*, May 2003.

[51] Jared Diamond, *Collapse: How Societes Choose to Fail or Succeed*, (New York: Penguin, 2004), as quoted in Senge, 26.

[52] Senge, 17.

[53] *Mail Online* (UK newspaper), "Found: The Monster of the My Lai Massacre," http://www.dailymail.co.uk/news/article-485983/Found-The-monster-My-Lai-massacre.html, (accessed Sept 2011).

[54] William Timothy O'Connell, "Military Dissent & Junior Officers" (student report, Air Command & Staff College, 1988), 4.

[55] Ibid., 2.

[55] Ibid., 3.

[57] Perlow, 2.

[58] Sophocles, *Antigone*, David R. Slavitt, trans. (New Haven: Yale Univ. Press), episode 3, 33.

[59] Fred Rogers, testimony before the Senate Subcommittee on Communications, circa 1969, at http://www.youtube.com/watch?v=yXEuEUQIP3Q (accessed Jan 2012).

[60] President Barack Obama, remarks, September 15, 2011, via http://www.whitehouse.gov/blog/2011/09/15/president-obama-awards-medal-honor-dakota-meyer (accessed Jan 2012).

[61] Attributed

[62] Attributed

[63] John of Salisbury, *The Metalogicon*, II.13.

[64] Louis P. Pojman, "Relativism," *The Cambridge Diction-ary of Philosophy*, Robert Audi, ed. (Cambridge, England: Cambridge University Press, 1995), 690.

[65] Attributed.

[66] George Orwell, "A Hanging," 1931.

[67] Joseph Ratzinger, *Pro Eligendo Romano Pontifice*, homily for funeral Mass of Pope John Paul the Great, April 18, 2005.

[68] Pojman, 690.

[69] *Exodus*: 20:1-17 and *Deuteronomy*: 5:4-21.

[70] U.S. Air Force, *Little Blue Book* (USAF, 1997), section II.

[71] Frank K. Magill, ed., *Masterpieces of World Philosophy* (New York: Harper Collins, 1990), 73.

[72] Will Durant, *The Story of Philosophy*, (New York: Simon & Schuster, 1991 ed.), 60.

[73] Robert E. Lee, letter to his wife, Dec 27, 1856.

[74] Abraham Lincoln, letter to A.G. Hodges, March 26, 1864.

[75] Magill, 77.

[76] Ibid., 77.

[77] Ibid., 76.

[78] Bryan Magee, *The Story of Philosophy* (London: Dorling Kindersley, 2008), 137.

[79] Bertrand Russell, *A History of Western Philosophy* (New York: Touchstone, 1972 ed.), 173.

[80] Bruce Russell, "Duty," *The Cambridge Dictionary of Philosophy*, 213.

[81] Roger Scruton, *A Short History of Modern Philosophy* (London: Routledge, 1995 ed.), 155.

[82] Ibid., 152, quoting Kant.

[83] Ibid., 152, quoting Kant.

[84] Dan W. Brock, "Utilitarianism," *The Cambridge Dictionary of Philosophy*, 824.

[85] Medal of Honor citation for Michael P. Murphy, 2007.

[86] Magill, ed., 403.

[87] Ibid., 404.

[88] Ibid., 404.

[89] Brock, 824.

[90] Thomas Aquinas, *Summa Theologica*, Second Part of the Second Part, Q. 40.

[91] Alan L. Lockwood, *The Case for Character Education: A Developmental Approach* (New York: Teachers College Press, 2009), 100.

[92] Attributed to Theodore Roosevelt by the Josephson Institute.

[93a] E.A. Wynne & H.J. Walberg, "The Complementary Goals of Character Development & Academic Excellence," *Educational Leadership*, vol. 43, issue 4, 15-18, via Lockwood, 26.

[93b] A. Kohn, *Punished by Rewards* (Boston: Houghton Mifflin, 1993).

[94] Lockwood, 29.

[95] W.C. Crain, *Theories of Development* (New York: Prentice Hall, 1985), 5.

[96] Attributed to James J. DiGiacome, SJ

[97] Op. cit. (same quote, excerpted).

[98] Steven A. Holmes, "James Stockdale, Perot's Running Mate in '92, Dies at 81," *New York Times*, July 6, 2005.

[99] Lockwood, 57-67.

[100] *A Christmas Story*, directed by Bob Clark, MGM, 1983.

[101] Crain, 1.

[102] Cain, 3.

[103] Perry M. Smith, *Rules & Tools for Leaders* (New York: Perigee, 2002), 49.

[104] William R. Cupach et al., *Competence in Interpersonal Conflict*, 2d ed. (Long Grove, IL: Waveland Press, 2010), 5.

[105] Ibid., 11.

[106] United Nations, *Charter of the United Nations*, Preamble.

[107] Cupach, 12.

[108] Morton Deutsch, *The Resolution of Conflict: Constructive & Destructive Processes* (New Haven, CT: Yale Press, 1973).

[109] Langston Hughes, "Harlem," 1951.

[110] Harry Webne-Behrman, "Conflict Resolution," University of Wisconsin-Madison, http://www.ohrd.wisc.edu/onlinetraining/resolution/index.asp, retrieved Nov 2009.

[111] Cupach, 33 ff.

[112] Cupach, 43.

[113] Cherie P. Shanteau et al., "Multi-Party Negotiation & Conflict Management Training Framework," HQ USAF, Office of the General Counsel, Nov 2005, p 30 (accessed Sept 2011).

[114] The majority of this section is excerpted verbatim from Dr. Stef Eisen, "Shortcuts to Cooperative Negotiating Strategies," Air Force Negotiation Center of Excellence (Maxwell AFB: Air University, 2011), with permission.

[115] Dr Stef Eisen, *Air Force Negotiation Center of Excellence*, negotiation.au.af.mil (accessed Sept 2011).

[116] Roger Fischer & William Ury, *Getting to Yes: Negotiating Agreement Without Giving In* (New York: Penguin, 1981).

[117] Attributed to Chester L. Karrass by the USAF Center for Negotiation Excellence, negotiation.au.af.mil.

[118] Shanteau et al., 14.

[119] Tolerance.Org, *Speak Up!* (Montgomery, AL: Southern Poverty Law Center, 2005) 78-81. Used with permission.

[120] Attributed by Tolerance.Org.

PHOTOS & PERMISSIONS
All photos are from Civil Air Patrol or public domain sources, unless noted otherwise.

2, 3 U.S. Air Force

4 U.S. Air Force

7 U.S. Army, National Archives, Library of Congress

8 The respective services via Wikimedia

9 U.S. Air Force Academy

11 U.S. Marine Corps via Google images

11 U.S. Coast Guard Academy via Wikimedia

11 U.S. Air Force Academy

11 U.S. Naval Academy via Flickr

11 Joint Staff via Flickr

11 U.S. Army

11 U.S. Air Force Academy

11 U.S. Air Force Academy

12 D-DAY: "June 6, 1944 -- The Climactic Battle of WWII" Author/ Editor: Stephen Ambrose, ISBN: 0-671-67334-3; Selection: Text excerpts from pp. 22-24

14 "Arab Spring" via Wikimedia

15 Roman legion via Google images

15 *Hogan's Heroes*, courtesy of Paramount via Landov Media

16 M&Ms via Google images

16 Replica of Frankenstrat used by Eddie Van Halen via Google images

16 Deepwater Horizon, U.S. Coast Guard via Wikimedia

17 Kroger via Google images

17 Macy's via Wikimedia

17 Safeway via Google images

17 Subaru via Google images

18 Kathy Lee Gifford via Shutterstock

19 Jayson Blair via Google images

19 Doris Kearns Goodwin via Google images

19 Marion Jones via Wikimedia

19 Rep. Joe Wilson via Google images

21 In the Hudson, via Wikimedia

21 "Captain Sully," via Google images

22 Hammer & Sickle via Wikimedia

22 Berlin Wall via Google images

22 Queen Victoria via Wikimedia

22 Nero via Wikimedia

22 Vexilloid of the Roman Empire via Google images

23 Nuremburg, U.S. Army photo via Wikimedia

23 Lieutenant William Calley, via Corbis

23 Gen Billy Mitchell courtesy of WI Aviation Hall of Fame, used with permission

24 Prince Edward of Wales, later Edward VIII, via Wikimedia as public domain

24 Edward Hopper, "Rooms by the Sea" via Yale University Art Gallery

25 "Mister Rogers" courtesy of Family Communications Inc.

25 US Capitol Building via Architect of the Capitol

25 Dakota Meyer, White House photo via Wikimedia

26 Valour & Cowardice by Alfred Stevens, Victoria & Albert Museum (V&A) 1857-66, London via Graham Spicer on flickr

26 The Thinker by Auguste Rodin (1840-1917) via Google images

28 Lincoln statue via Wikimedia

29 Dogs, courtesy of the author, their friend

29 Jenelle Armstrong Byrd, "Lance Sijan," US Air Force Academy via Google images

31 Immanuel Kant via Wikimedia

31 Crown of Scotland via Google images

32 Pierre Vivant, "Traffic Light Tree" via Google images

32 View from Bondcliff, White Mountain National Forest via Google images

32 Crowded House in concert, via Google images

32 Motor vehicle accident via Wikimedia

32 Cessna

33 dodlive.mil

34 Triumph Motorcycles

35 Ground Zero, Federal Emergency Management Agency, via Wikimedia

35 Theodore Roosevelet, via Wikimedia

37 Imitation of Michaelangelo's "Delphic Sibyl" via Google Images

37 VADM James B. Stockdale, via US Navy

38 "Brian and Chewy," courtesy of the author

39 *A Christmas Story* © Turner Entertainment Co. A Warner Bros. Entertainment Company. All Rights Reserved.

40 Flag outside United Nations via Google images

40 United Nations General Assembly Hall via Wikimedia

41 "Harlem (2)" from THE COLLECTED POEMS OF LANGSTON HUGHES by Langston Hughes, edited by Arnold Rampersad with David Roessel, Associate Editor, copyright © 1994 by the Estate of Langston Hughes. Used by permission of Alfred A. Knopf, a division of Random House, Inc.

41 Langston Hughes via Literature Wikispaces

42 Gerhard Marcks, "Hiob," via Wikimedia

43 US Navy via Wikimedia

44 "Occupy Wall Street" David Shankbone via Wikimedia

44 "The Troubles" via Wikimedia

45 Millard Fillmore via Wikimedia

45 Franklin Pierce via Wikimedia

45 James Buchanan via Smithsonian Art Museum

45 Union Soldiers at Fredericksburg, Virginia 1863 via Wikimedia

48 "Warrior / Negotiator" via Department of Defense

48 *American Pickers* courtesy of Loey L via Google images

48 *Pawn Stars* via Google images

50 Auschwitz, via Wikimedia

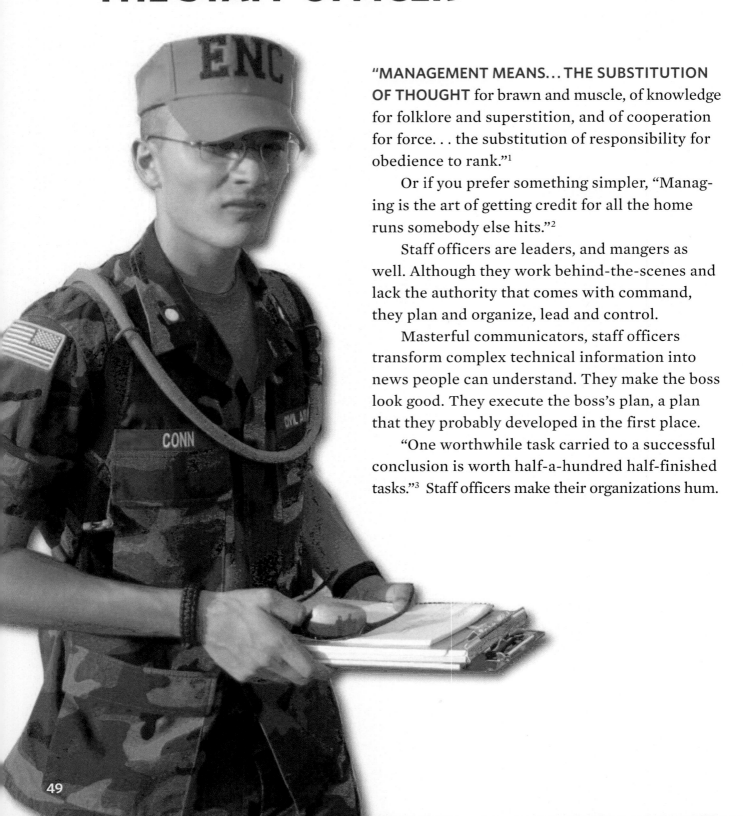

CHAPTER 10
THE STAFF OFFICER

"MANAGEMENT MEANS... THE SUBSTITUTION OF THOUGHT** for brawn and muscle, of knowledge for folklore and superstition, and of cooperation for force. . . the substitution of responsibility for obedience to rank."[1]

Or if you prefer something simpler, "Managing is the art of getting credit for all the home runs somebody else hits."[2]

Staff officers are leaders, and mangers as well. Although they work behind-the-scenes and lack the authority that comes with command, they plan and organize, lead and control.

Masterful communicators, staff officers transform complex technical information into news people can understand. They make the boss look good. They execute the boss's plan, a plan that they probably developed in the first place.

"One worthwhile task carried to a successful conclusion is worth half-a-hundred half-finished tasks."[3] Staff officers make their organizations hum.

ORGANIZATIONS & THE STAFF OFFICER

In the military, perhaps one officer in fifty serves in a command position. The remaining officers are staff officers. In this section, we consider the role of the staff officer. But before getting into the practical matters of staff work, let's pause to discuss the entity in which staff officers serve: the organization.

THE ORGANIZATION AS A FORMAL TEAM

OBJECTIVE:

1. Define the term "organization."

What is an Organization?   As introduced in chapter 2, teams are groups of people who work together toward a common goal. Organizations take this idea a step further. An organization is a body of individuals working under a defined system of rules, assignments, procedures, and relationships designed to achieve identifiable goals and objectives.[4]

A handful of guys who push a stalled car out of a busy intersection are a team. The U.S. Air Force, with its formal chain of command; formal rules and regulations; formal job titles and duty assignments; formal procedures for dropping iron on target; and formal, carefully crafted mission statements and goals and objectives is an organization that endures. A staff officer serves within the context of a formal organization.

Teams & Organizations. The guys pushing the car are a *team*. The USAFA Prep School cadets are part of a team, too, but even more they belong to an *organization* with formal goals, rules, and procedures.

CHAPTER GOALS

1. Understand the effects of organizational structure on determining roles for staff officers.

2. Recall the fundamentals of leadership using committees.

3. Summarize the role of a staff officer with regard to ethics and project management.

4. Demonstrate effective communication skills for online, written, and spoken presentations.

THE FIVE COMPONENTS OF AN ORGANIZATION

OBJECTIVE:

2.   Identify the five components of an organization.

While a team is simply a single entity known as "the team," an organization is much more complex, consisting of five basic parts in two groupings.[5]

STRATEGIC APEX

TECHNOSTRUCTURE   SUPPORT STAFF

MIDDLE LINE

OPERATING CORE

The five components of an organization

The Line is the first of two groupings. The line is the chain of workers and leaders who directly accomplish the organization's mission. It is comprised of three parts.

The Operating Core performs the organization's basic work. They are the front-line workers and foot soldiers whose efforts directly affect the organization's accomplishment of its mission. In a cadet squadron, the in-ranks cadets are the operating core.

The Middle Line has direct authority over the operating core. Serving as a link between the front-line workers and the top leaders, middle line leaders pass information up and down the chain. More importantly, they interpret ideas conceived at the strategic apex, develop plans for completing their piece of the puzzle, and explain how the operating core is to execute those plans. The middle line allocates the resources (money, equipment, people, etc.) that flow down from the organization's headquarters. In effect, the middle line leader "performs all the managerial roles of the chief executive, but in the context of managing his or her own unit."[6] In a cadet squadron, the cadet flight commanders and cadet commander comprise the middle line.

The Strategic Apex presides over the entire organization and exercises authority over the whole operation. The central figure is the commander, company president, or business owner, but the term also includes the handful of the most senior leaders who work closely with the boss – the vice commanders, vice presidents, directors, and the like. This small leadership team formulates the strategy by which the organization fulfills its mission. (It may be useful to review the strategic, operational, and tactical arenas discussed in chapter 4.) The strategic apex allocates resources to the subordinate parts of the organization. Senior leaders at this level cope with the big decisions affecting the organization, either making those decisions themselves, or ratifying the recommendations offered by subordinates. They are spokespeople representing the organization to the most prominent customers and stakeholders outside the organization. And of course, they ensure the overall organization functions as a single, well-oiled machine. The strategic apex has the widest scope of responsibilities, and its work is the most abstract of the five basic parts of the organization. In a cadet squadron, the squadron commander and his or her deputies comprise the strategic apex.

The Staff is the second of two groupings. The staff does not directly accomplish the organization's mission, but provides technical and administrative support to the line that does. There are two parts to the staff.

The Technostructure is the group of specialists who help standardize the organization. They design programs, plan new initiatives, and issue technical directions about the work that the middle line and operating core performs. These "gurus" have deep knowledge of a functional area, that is, an aspect of the organization's mission. Although the technostructure lacks direct authority over the line, they formulate policies and procedures relating to their functional area that the strategic apex can impose on the middle line and operating core. This soft authority is sometimes called functional authority. Because of their deep, technical knowledge about the organization's mission (or at least one corner of it), the technostructure can mentor the middle line in the technical aspects of the job. Staffers serving within the technostructure find themselves at the intersection of the strategic apex above them, the middle line beside them, and the operating core beside and below them. Therefore, they need to coordinate their activities up and down and across the chain of command. In a cadet squadron, the aerospace education officer, leadership officer, and emergency services officer (and sometimes other officers) comprise the technostructure.

The Support Staff is the group of specialists who provide administrative, financial, logistical, and other support to the mission areas of the organization. Note that the support staff's expertise is not directly related to the mission itself, while the technostructure's expertise is. Support staff do not exercise formal authority over the line, but they do set rules and procedures for how they serve the line and administer their area of responsibility. Despite the fact that the support staff does not directly accomplish the mission, their services are still essential. Consider the infantryman fighting a war in the desert. He is the operating core. But without cooks, he starves. Without accountants, he does not get paid. Without logisticians, he runs out of bullets. The support staff is essential, though their efforts support the mission indirectly. In a cadet squadron, the finance officer, administrative officer, personnel officer, transportation officer, supply officer, and others comprise the support staff.

Traditional Cadetspeak vs. Technical Terminology

CADET CURRY: "This summer, I'll be on encampment staff."

CADET ARNOLD: "Great. How so?"

CADET CURRY: "I'm gonna be a flight commander."

CADET ARNOLD: "Huh? I thought you were staff, not line."

In a casual sense, *staff* can imply being part of a cadre, a member of an organization's overall leadership team.

In cadetspeak, *staff* cadets are the cadets who are not mere in-ranks cadets.

But in truth, only the technical and support people are *staff* commanders, deputies, flight sergeants, and the like, are part of the *line*.

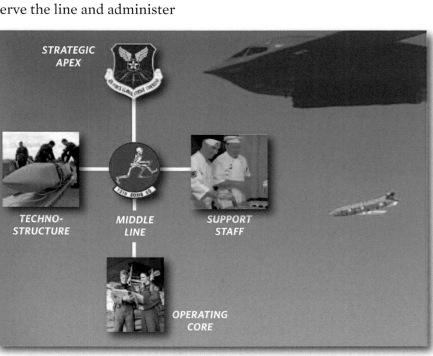

HIERARCHY OR CHAOS?

OBJECTIVES:

3. Discuss four reasons that support the use of hierarchical organizational structures.
4. Discuss two reasons that support the use of free-form organizational structures.

Must an organization be organized? The very term *organization* implies a team whose people and operations are arranged into a formal, carefully coordinated structure. But some management theorists urge leaders to become renegades who embrace chaos. Throw out the wiring diagram or formal chain of command, they say. Make the organization "free form." Outlined below is an argument for hierarchy and structure, and an argument for chaos and a free-flowing staff arrangement.

THE CASE FOR HIERARCHICAL ORGANIZATIONAL STRUCTURES

Back in chapter 1, we discussed hierarchical organizational structures by explaining what a chain of command is and why the chain is useful. Now it is time for a more sophisticated study of the pyramid of superiors and subordinates that we will refer to as hierarchy.

Hierarchies Promote Accountability. One assumption about hierarchy is that a job will not get done without someone being accountable for it. Proponents of hierarchy would say it is naïve to believe that a team that lacks a formal leader will get the job done on time and up to standards. "Group authority without group accountability is dysfunctional," says one expert, "and group authority with group accountability is unacceptable."[7] In other words, groups need a single leader who is held accountable for the group's actions.

Hierarchies Allocate Authority. If someone has responsibility for an area of the organization, he or she will require the authority to run that team or program. One expert explains, "Authority flows from accountability in the sense that there should be just that amount of authority needed to discharge the accountability."[8] A hierarchical organizational structure (i.e., a formal chain of command) is a system for allocating authority.

Hierarchies Are Easy to Manage. A leader can effectively control only so many people, projects, and priorities at once. The term "span of control" refers to the number of subordinates reporting to one supervisor.[9] Leaders who are overloaded with responsibilities will

The Air Force's A-Staff

A1 Manpower and Personnel
A2 Intelligence
A3 Air, Space & Information Operations
A4 Logistics
A5 Plans and Requirements
A6 Communications
A7 Installations & Mission Support
A8 Strategic Plans & Programs
A9 Analyses, Assessments, & Lessons Learned

By adopting an alphanumeric staff structure, the Air Force made it easier for leaders at one Air Force unit to contact their counterparts at another, let alone a unit in one of the other services.

One officer explains, "One command might have called [the manpower office] the A5M, another the XPM, and still another the DPM." Now with all the services following the same basic alphanumeric staff structure, military members find it easier to talk with their counterparts.[10]

In huge organizations like the Department of Defense, a great deal of structure and standardization is needed just so people can get their bearings and find their way around the organization.

Hierarchy. A system or organization in which people or groups are ranked one above the other according to status or authority.[11] In management texts, you will also see the term *scalar* used. Both terms refer to a pyramid of superiors and subordinates.

have to let some items in their portfolio go unattended. Hierarchies leave managers with a reasonable span of control because other leaders in the hierarchy carry some of the burden.

Hierarchies Create Efficiencies. Through a hierarchical system, the organization becomes a team of teams. Those sub-teams are able to specialize – a finance department works only on finance issues, a sales department works only on sales. That specialization results in improved job performance. Moreover, this arrangement creates economies of scale. Would the Air Force fly, fight, and win better if pilots focused on flying, or if each pilot had to maintain his or her aircraft, plow the runway after a snowstorm, and negotiate fuel prices?

In short, it seems impossible to lead an organization of more than a handful of people without resorting to some kind of hierarchical system. Is it any wonder that the common sense benefits of hierarchies have been known to leaders for centuries, as illustrated in the sidebar at right?

THE CASE FOR THRIVING ON CHAOS

Bloated, expensive hierarchies are all wrong. To be a great leader, you have to know how to thrive on chaos. This is the organizational philosophy of leadership renegade Tom Peters. Toss out the pyramid of superiors and subordinates and allow the organization to be free-form. A limited structure will arise spontaneously. The characteristics of the free form organization are best understood by focusing on how the role of the first-line supervisor changes:[12]

First-Line Supervisor in the "Old" Hierarchical System	First-Line Supervisor of Free-Form System of Self-Directed Teams
10 people directly report to him or her	50 to 70 direct reports
Scheduler of work	Coach and sounding board for the self-managing team; emphasis is on training and improving people
Rule enforcer; catches people doing things wrong and disciplines them	Facilitator who gets experts to help the teams as needed
Lots of planning	Lots of wandering and "management by walking around"
Focuses vertically; works issues "up" and "down" the chain	Focuses horizontally, working with other teams and functions to speed things up and get things done
Transmits the top and middle managers' needs down the chain to the troops	Sells the team's ideas and needs "up" and "across" the organization to the other teams and functions
Provides new ideas for the troops; is the fount of knowledge and wisdom	Helps the team members develop their own ideas; provides ideas on how to work together better, smarter, and cheaper

Economies of Scale. When all input quantities are increased by X percent, the quantity of output rises by more than X percent.[14] If you buy a package of hot dogs at the store, you pay $3. A school cafeteria buys by the case or pallet and pays far less per package due to economies of scale.

Hierarchies Get in the Way. Peters argues that hierarchical structures are necessarily slow to change because good ideas get stalled at each successive level of bureaucracy. We get rules for the sake of rules, processes for the sake of processes that only protect the entrenched interests of non-contributing middle managers and inefficient support staffs. Bureaucracy impedes the sense of urgency that the team needs to win. Hierarchical structures mistakenly see the "boss" at the top of the pyramid, instead of at the bottom where he or she belongs, as a servant leader.

Free-Form, Self-Directed Teams Are Agile. Peters believes that the free-form, self-directed team is more adaptable and more effective in responding to the needs of the market. In contrast, when customers encounter rigid hierarchies, they may seek help from several employees, each of whom dismisses the customer's problem with the "that's not my department" attitude. The following scenario illustrates Peters' point:

> *You're taking a long hike in the mountains and will stay overnight at a remote hut that provides dinner. When making your reservation online, you add a note, "I require a special vegetarian meal," and provide the details.*
>
> *To double-check that they'll meet your needs, you call the establishment a week in advance to make arrangements. "We handle vegetarians all the time," the sales agent tells you, when you get to base camp, just tell the desk clerk what you need."*
>
> *At base camp, the registration clerk tells you, "Dining issues are not my department. Check with the hut's crew when you arrive there tonight."*
>
> *Departing base camp, off you go into the woods on your hike. Several hours later you reach the remote mountain hut. You find the cook and ask about your special meal. "It's too darn late now to make special requests!" he admonishes. "You should've made arrangements in advance."*
>
> *But you did! You interacted with the company multiple times, but in each instance the organizational hierarchy passed the buck. Will this experience make you a loyal customer?*

Imagine if the company was not structured as a hierarchy, but a free-form, self-directed team. The reservations agent, the desk clerk at base camp, and the crew at the remote mountain hut all knew the names of their guests for the coming evening, their arrival and departure itineraries, their special meal requests. Any one person you encountered would have been able to either confirm that your special meal was all set, or would have noticed the problem in time

RING A BELL IF IT'S TIME FOR A RE-ORG

The British created a civil service job in 1803 calling for a man to stand on the cliffs of Dover with a spyglass. He was supposed to ring a bell if he saw Napoleon coming.

The job was abolished in 1945.[15]

Organizational re-designs can be traumatic upheavals for all involved. Therefore leaders should not reorganize their teams willy-nilly. But when the organization's mission, strategy, size, or complexity changes, the organization's design should, too.[16] It's a safe bet that Napoleon won't be attacking anytime soon.

Will dinner be ready? In a hierarchical organization, it will be *only* if you speak with the right person. But with a free-form, self-directed team, everyone you encounter is empowered to get the job done.

to fix it. Free-form, self-directed teams are non-hierarchical. Their quickness and agility unleash their power to win.

ORGANIZATIONAL DESIGN: A FINAL WORD

Should your organization be structured hierarchically, or should you embrace chaos? One respected expert says this is a false dilemma. There is no perfect organizational structure.[17] Organizations need both hierarchy and free-form teams, task forces, and the freedom to morph to do a new job, then morph back to the traditional structure again.[18] Again, the organization's structure should follow its current strategy, and change as needed. But how do you know if your organization's structure is a good fit? Performance, naturally. Performance is the test of an organization's structure.[19]

The CREATIVE INDEPENDENCE of SMALL ORGANIZATIONS

Nataly Dawn & Jack Conte of *Pomplamoose*

Synergy, you will recall from chapter 2, is the principle that people can achieve more together than they could on their own. Synergy makes 1 + 1 = 3. Does it follow then that the more people who join the effort make the growing team that much more successful? Is the biggest team the best?

Pomplamoose, a musical duo of Jack Conte and Nataly Dawn, is proving that artists can thrive on their own, without the backing of a record label's large organization. The band finds its audience via YouTube, and sells its music via iTunes.

True, YouTube, owned by Google, and iTunes, owned by Apple, are massive, multi-national organizations. Still, *Pomplamoose* comes closer than anyone toward taking their music directly to their fans. Jack and Nataly write the music and the lyrics. Jack and Nataly record their performances and produce their video songs on their

own. Jack and Nataly upload their videos and MP3s to the web.

In contrast, for the first sixty years of rock, artists desperately needed the record labels. Not even the greatest musicians could survive without a label backing them. Record companies recorded and produced the

"Just go online and do it yourself."

music. Record companies manufactured physical albums, cassettes, or CDs. Record companies distributed the physical albums to physical stores. Record companies counted the sales and computed the profits. Musicians couldn't survive without surrendering a part of themselves to large, formal, hierarchical organizations.

With all those middle-men supporting the artists, did the artists find synergy? Not often. One critic tells

the story of a band that "made the music industry more than three million dollars richer, but is in the hole . . . on royalties. The band members each earned about a third as much as they would working at a 7-Eleven, but they got to ride in a tour bus for a month."[20]

Pomplamoose has shown that small, independent artists can thrive in the digital age.

"People think that all of these things have to be done by geniuses behind huge desks or at the top of skyscrapers," explains Nataly Dawn, "but you can just go online and do it yourself."[21]

THE STAFF OFFICER'S ULTIMATE CHALLENGE: EXECUTIVE OFFICER or EXECUTIVE ASSISTANT

Behind every great senior leader is a crack executive officer (in a military setting) or executive assistant (in a corporate setting).

The "XO" is the commander's direct, personal aide. Serving as an XO or executive assistant is often a tremendous career broadening experience because you get to see how senior leaders think and act, and you become familiar with the challenges facing the organization at the highest levels. Not surprisingly then, the lieutenants and captains who serve as XOs in the military often go on to prestigious assignments as majors and beyond.

To be an effective XO or executive assistant, you need to know how to "manage up." That is, know how to manage your boss or lead him or her from behind. What are some of the principles for managing up?[22]

1. Make life easier for the boss. This is the primary purpose of the XO or executive assistant. Work hard to free up the boss's time and energy so he or she can focus on those things that only the boss can do.

2. Place the boss's agenda first, period. As an XO, your personal career interests and aspirations have to come second. Know that when your boss wins, you win. And if you make your boss look good, in time he or she will help you move up, too.

3. Equip the boss with the information needed to make decisions. Create time for the boss, and likewise, keep time killers at bay. For example, the XO receives documents that subordinate commanders want routed to the boss. Simply passing them along adds no value to the process. Ask, "What is the main issue in this document? What is the boss being asked to do? How does this document or project relate to the other issues on the boss's desk? Will the boss have questions about this document, and if so, does the document answer them effectively?" Instead of being a simple mailman, help the boss by screening documents so that only completed staff work reaches his desk.

4. Prepare the boss for all meetings. Look at his or her calendar and stay a few days ahead of the boss, so you can be sure your boss is ready for whatever challenges are on the horizon.

• What is the purpose of meeting?

• Does the boss have a copy of the agenda?

• Where and when is the event? What is the proper attire?

• What background info is important for the boss to know to participate in the meeting?

• Will the boss need input from his or her staff prior to attending the event?

• Are there other items that are important to the boss that he or she would like covered during the meeting?

5. Frequently update the boss via short, face-to-face encounters. An in-person approach is usually more efficient than email because it allows for the quick give-and-take of questions and answers.

6. Keep confidential information confidential. An XO becomes privy to sensitive information. Maybe someone is about to be fired. Maybe the organization is about to launch a new strategy or new initiative. People are apt to press you for inside information. Don't feed the rumor mill; protect confidential information.

7. Help edit all documents. Ensure that all documents that are published under the boss's signature are clear, concise, and proofread thoroughly. Part of making your boss look good means ensuring every memo, presentation, and report is perfect.

8. Keep the boss on track. If necessary, be a helpful nag. Be persistent and offer timely reminders of the incomplete tasks remaining on the boss's "to do" list.

9. Resist the urge to "wear" the boss's rank. Remember that you are simply the XO, a staff assistant, albeit a powerful one. Do not carry yourself as if you are the boss. Respect the senior leaders who often go through you to reach the boss. Do not presume to give orders to anyone, but merely relay the boss's directions.

10. Own your mistakes. In a small team such as a boss/XO relationship, there's no place to hide mistakes. Eventually they will come out. Therefore, be forthright and bring your mistakes to the boss's attention right away so that he or she can readjust the plan accordingly. Simply say, "Hey boss, sorry I goofed…" or "Boss, before you hear it from someone else, I need to tell you . . ."

KEY PRINCIPLES of ORGANIZATIONAL THEORY

Each component of the organization (i.e., each team, department, unit, etc.) should work to support the organization's overall strategy. Strategy comes first, and the organizational structure should be designed to support the strategy.[23]

Organize so that your best people can focus on the major decisions, key activities, and on performance and results.[24]

Build the fewest possible management levels and forge the shortest possible chain of command.[25]

The more flexible the organizational structure, the more disciplined and stronger the team members have to be.[26]

The different components of an organization can be organized differently, in response to their unique situations and local needs.[27]

Choose the least costly and least difficult process for coordinating among sub-units and components to get the job done.[28]

An organization should be as complex as its business requires.[29]

Organizations can be designed so that managers have simple roles in a complex structure, or work in a simple structure but have highly complex jobs.[30]

Note that the position of XO is quite different in a military environment, compared to the XO's role in a cadet setting.

LEADERSHIP IN COMMITTEE

"Deliver us from committees."[31]

ROBERT FROST

"I've searched all the parks in all the cities — and found no statues of Committees."[32]

GK CHESTERTON

Committees are a common venue for leadership. Congress operates via committee. University departments govern themselves as committees. Every Fortune 500 company is directed by a committee. The accused stand trial before a jury, a committee of one's peers. Homeowners' associations, churches, student clubs, civic groups, and countless other everyday institutions use committees. As a leader, you can expect that in the course of your personal and professional life you will serve on many committees. Therefore, anyone who aspires to any sort of leadership role must develop committee-leading skills.

COMMITTEES AS VEHICLES FOR LEADERSHIP

OBJECTIVES:
5. Define the term "committee."
6. List three reasons why leadership by committee can be helpful.

From this point in your cadet career forward, nearly all the work you will accomplish will be as a member of a small team. As Margaret Mead has pointed out, small groups of "thoughtful, committed citizens can change the world." For our purposes, a committee is a group of people entrusted to study issues, make recommendations or decisions, or perform some kind of service to a larger group. Thus, a small team can also be defined as a committee. What are some of the reasons for committees being used as vehicles for leadership?

Good Ideas Can Come from Anybody. First, anybody's viewpoint could be valuable; high-ranking leaders do not have a monopoly on good ideas. Nearly all good ideas result from the diversity of the group. If that principle is true, it makes sense to not simply tolerate low-level subordinates contributing to leadership discussions, but for organizations to aggressively seek input from everyone who could have something to contribute. Committees provide a venue for doing that.

Benefits of Specialization

By specializing in one or two facets of an issue, committees and subcommittees develop incredible expertise. As a result, the overall organization gets smarter and can make more enlightened decisions.

Committees Can Be Smarter Than Individuals.
Second, there is some evidence to suggest that
groups can make better decisions than individuals.
Although the populist view of leadership presumes
the command-and-control mindset where a single,
decisive leader charges to victory, there is great
danger in allowing a single individual to decide
some matters on his or her own. The jury system,
for example, was created so that no one person
could send you to jail. In the safety arena, a small
group of people pre-flighting an obstacle course
or discussing the plan for a trek into the wilderness is more apt to
identify potential hazards than a single individual.[33] Groups can be
smarter than the individual leader.

Group Action Adds Legitimacy to Decisions. Third, people are more
likely to support, or at least accept, the decisions they had a voice in
creating. Committees give people a voice, a seat at the table. Citizens
of western democracies may complain about their governments, but
they recognize the government's basic legitimacy because the massive
committee called the electorate voted the leaders into office. Moreover, a committee-style group decision-making process promoted
unity among the Chilean miners who were trapped underground for
ten weeks in 2010. "Everything was voted on….," reported one of the
survivors. "We were 33 men, so 16 plus one was a majority."[34] Even
after rescue, committee-style leadership continued. The survivors
all agreed to consult with one another before speaking with the
worldwide media clamoring for their stories. Committees create a
sense of unity that can withstand stressful times and dissenting views.

The Power of Group Decisions

On the popular TV show,
Project Runway, a panel confers
about the contestants' fashion
designs, then announces the
winner and loser.

If a designer fails to impress
one particular panelist, he or
she still has a chance to win
because three other panelists
have a say in the group's final
decision.

Group-based decisions reflect
a sense of majority rule,
adding a legitimacy that a
single person's decision does
not have, no matter how wise
that individual may be.

OPPORTUNITIES FOR COMMITTEE LEADERSHIP

OBJECTIVES:

7.   Define the term "standing committee."
8.   Define the term "select committee."
9.   List five triggers that alert an organization to begin using a
     committee.

When should organizations form committees? There are at least five
different triggers that warrant an organization putting committee-
style leadership in motion.

In-Depth Discussion. When the issues are complex, nuanced, and
easy to get wrong, committees can provide a service by studying the
issue in detail. The larger organization benefits because it can proceed with the other challenges on its agenda.

Manageable Group Size. Democratic principles are not always easy to uphold in the real world. Discussions among ten individuals are difficult enough; discussions among one hundred people are virtually impossible on practical grounds. Committees make democratic leadership principles easier to manage simply by virtue of the group size being smaller than the overall organization.

Division of Labor. Busy, ambitious organizations take on several challenges simultaneously. Committees help the organization by allowing a division of labor. The leadership burden is shared when one committee takes ownership of one slice of the organization's challenges, and another committee focuses upon a different slice of the organization.

Specialization & Expertise. Committee systems raise the overall organization's collective intelligence. By specializing in one or two facets of the organization, committee members become seasoned experts in those subtopics. As a result, the organization makes decisions that are smarter, and better informed.

Special Handling. Some matters require discreet handling. Personnel issues, national intelligence matters, and mergers and acquisitions are examples. Committees enable the overall group to maintain both a degree of confidentiality and democratic leadership.

MEETINGS:
WHERE COMMITTEES GET THE JOB DONE

OBJECTIVES:
10. Describe six tools leaders can use to ensure productive committee meetings.
11. Identify ways to contribute politely during web, phone, and video conferences.
12. List some helpful tips for meeting etiquette.

"A committee is a group that keeps minutes and wastes hours."[35]

MILTON BERLE

Individual members of the committee might complete some of the committee's work on their own, but eventually a committee must convene to discuss its business. The venue for doing so is the committee meeting. What are some guidelines leaders can use to ensure meetings are productive?

Goal Statements. Is this meeting really necessary? Before calling a meeting, the committee leader, chairperson, or boss should ask, "What is this meeting intended to achieve?," "What would happen if

Government

Business

The Military

Committees are Everywhere
Leadership by committee often gets a bad rap. And yet the president relies upon a committee – his cabinet – for leadership (top), the economy is controlled by a committee – the Federal Reserve Board of Governors, (middle), and the military is run by a committee – the Joint Chiefs of Staff (bottom).

we didn't meet?," and "How will we know if the meeting is a success or failure?"[36] When requesting the meeting and when calling the meeting to order, the committee leader should express the purpose of the meeting in a concise goal statement.

Objective-Driven Agendas. The agenda is the key document driving the meeting. When published in advance, agendas enable participants to arrive at the meeting fully prepared to accomplish the meeting's goals. On a simplistic level, an agenda is merely a list of topics that the committee will work through, perhaps with some hint as to how much time will be devoted to each. While that method may work for the briefest, most casual meetings, such a vague approach is bound to make any meeting of substance ineffective. The most effective agendas are objective-driven. They don't merely list topics; they identify actions and outcomes. See the sidebar for examples.

Read-Aheads. Information that is purely factual should be distributed via email. Presenting factual information orally not only wastes the committee's precious time, but requires the audience to take notes and possibly make errors in the process. On a more positive note, read-aheads – documents that provide background and context about an issue – make discussions more fruitful because they allow participants to absorb the key information in advance and then devote the meeting time to discussion, not mere information transfer. One expert observes, "The act of writing sentences and preparing a [read-ahead] will make for smarter reports."[37] The result is shorter meetings, discussions that get to the heart of the issue, and better group decisions.

Oral Presentations. Sometimes purely factual information requires special handling. Perhaps a particular individual should deliver the news ("I'm resigning as squadron commander because our family is moving away"). Or if the matter is delicate, an oral delivery helps ensure the message strikes just the right tone and emphasizes just the right nuances, while also allowing for immediate questions and answers. Finally, some information is important in that it provides context. Email messages go unread if the subject line seems irrelevant to an individual recipient, but during the course of an oral presentation, that same individual may discover an unforeseen connection between her area of responsibility and the topic at hand.

Agenda Sequencing & Breakouts. It is common for groups to be most energetic at the beginning of a meeting. Therefore, the chairperson may find it useful to place the most critical topics toward the top of the agenda. Likewise, if the least important items are scheduled last, they may be postponed if the meeting runs out of time. A similar

MEETING ETIQUETTE [38]

The chairperson articulates a clear goal for the meeting.

The chair keeps meetings as brief as possible, partly by distributing factual information in advance.

All participants come prepared to contribute, having completed any "homework" assignments.

All participants attend the meetings they have committed to.

All participants arrive on time and remain until the end.

All participants focus on the business at hand, not their laptops or phones.

All participants listen respectfully during discussions, and wait their turn to speak.

issue is the use of breakout or off-line discussions. If an issue affects only a minority of the group, the committee might work through all topics of mutual interest first, then conclude the meeting (as far as the full committee is concerned), after which that minority of concerned people deal with their business apart from the full committee. Behind this basic philosophy of agenda sequencing and breakout sessions is the belief that meetings should respect each individual's time by being as brief as possible.

Closings & Minutes. Time spent recapping a meeting's results is time well spent. Before closing the meeting, the chair orally summarizes what was decided, and the committee's and/or each individual member's next steps. Who is responsible for doing what, and by when? This is also the time to identify the issues that remain on the committee's docket, and when and where the committee will meet next. If an oral summary is insufficient, meeting minutes – a written summary of the meeting's outcomes – provide a more substantial record. Minutes can be a simple listing of key decisions, or an in-depth record of all discussions, parliamentary procedures, and voting results. In the context of a staff officer working on projects and conducting routine business, the general practice is to keep minutes succinct and for the chairperson or scribe to email the notes to all participants within a few days - the sooner the better.

Time is Money
Goal statements, objective-driven agendas, read aheads, and accurate minutes are tools that make meetings effective, not wastes of time and money.

TOPICAL VS. OBJECTIVE-DRIVEN AGENDAS

A topical agenda is simply a list of topics to somehow be covered during a meeting. This topical agenda tells us little. What does the committee hope to accomplish in these areas? If given an agenda in this form, chances are you'll have no idea what you should do to prepare.

Meeting Agenda

1. Color Guard
2. Day Hike
3. Cadet of the Month

An objective-driven agenda specifies what the committee will accomplish. It still includes a list of topics, but goes a step further by identifying the desired outcomes. Action verbs start each sentence (e.g., create, receive, examine, select). The outcomes are the phrases that follow those action verbs. At the end of the meeting, as the committee reviews the agenda, if they can answer, "Yes, we did that," then everyone can be confident that the meeting was successful.

Meeting Agenda

1800-1810 hrs. C/MSgt Goddard
Color Guard: For Discussion & Action

Create a schedule for practices and identify three community events to participate in during the calendar year.

1810-1815 hrs. C/2d Lt Mitchell
Day Hike: For Information

Receive briefing on trip itinerary, safety considerations, and training goals.

1815-1825 hrs. C/Capt Earhart
Cadet of the Month: For Decision

Examine the raw scores, discuss individual cadets' performance, and select the winner.

TELECONS, WEBCHATS, & VIDEOCONFERENCES

Meetings held via teleconference or online have special challenges. It is easy for participants to get distracted because of the lack of face-to-face interaction. Conversations can be tough to manage because visual cues are not available to guide the flow, or signal whose turn it is to speak. Background noise and secondary activities taking place at each individual's location interfere with the group's discussion. Listed below are some guidelines to help telecons, webchats, and videoconferences succeed.

Teleconferences

Place yourself in a quiet space, free from distractions

Be ready to receive the call precisely on time, if not a few minutes early

State your name before speaking

Make a special effort to be clear and concise

Identify the person to whom you are responding, or to whom you are directing a question

Announce if departing from the call early; announce yourself upon returning to the call

Web Chats with Audio & Text Capability

Be online and ready to accept the chat / call precisely on time, if not a few minutes early

If a new user of the technology, try to test your connection and software in advance

Place yourself in a quiet space, free from distractions

Mute your microphone when not speaking

Type a period "." in the text chat to indicate your desire to speak

Turn down your speaker volume when speaking, to avoid audio feedback

Offer parenthetical remarks in the text chat, not orally

Provide web links via the text chat, if referencing a document

Videoconferences[39]

If a new user of the technology, try to test your connection and software in advance

Dress as you would for an in-person meeting

Place yourself in a quiet space, free from distractions

Make eye contact with and speak directly to the camera

Avoid side conversations; if you absolutely have to discuss something privately, mute your speaker

TYPES OF COMMITTEES

Standing Committee
A committee that operates continuously and has an indefinite charter.

Select Committee
A committee that is established on a temporary basis, usually to consider a one-time issue. These committees disband once their work is completed. Some select committees of the U.S. Congress became standing committees or have operated for many years, becoming standing committees in effect.

LEADERSHIP CHALLENGES FOR MEETING FACILITATORS & COMMITTEE CHAIRS

OBJECTIVES:

13. Define the job of a meeting facilitator.
14. Defend the idea of the committee chairperson or meeting facilitator as a servant leader.
15. Identify four hallmarks of facilitative leadership.
16. List eight tips a facilitative leader can use to actively manage a group discussion.

Process-Focus vs. Content-Focus Like a flight line marshaller, a committee chair is process-focused, not content focused. The chair's concern is in starting the engines on time and taxiing to the right runway, not the aircraft's final destination.

Facilitative Leadership. The individuals who preside over meetings and committees serve a facilitative role. The job of facilitators is to "evoke the best possible performance from each member of their team."[40] They are *process-focused,* not *content-focused.* That is, they are responsible for creating the conditions so that the group can thoroughly engage the issues via discussions, find the best possible solution, and build consensus for that solution. Members of the committee or team (not the chair) take responsibility for content and for studying the issues and hashing out workable solutions.

Joys & Challenges of the Chair. Reflecting on the joys and perks of being a chairperson, one expert wrote, "There is, in fact, only one legitimate source of pleasure in chairmanship, and that is pleasure in the achievements of the meeting – and to be legitimate it must be shared by all those present."[41] Immature leaders may be tempted to dominate the committees and meetings they "command." Again, that same expert advises, "It is the chairman's self-indulgence that is the greatest single barrier to the success of a meeting. His first duty . . . is to be aware of the temptation [to dominate]."[42] If you chair a meeting and hear yourself talking more than anyone else, step back; you've become too much of a domineering force.

"WAS I ASKING FOR YOUR OPINION!?!!!?"
The authoritarian leadership style is out of place in a committee setting, where the whole point is to promote a lively sharing of ideas.

CHAIRPERSON AS FACILITATOR & SERVANT LEADER

An authoritarian or domineering leadership style is out of place in a committee setting. After all, the whole point is to harness the group's collective knowledge to win. Therefore, the facilitative leadership style requires an unassuming, collaborative spirit, where the leader stands back and gently redirects the group or prompts enquiry into new lines of thought. His or her role is to serve the team, not command it. Some of the hallmarks of facilitative leadership include:[43]

A Neutral Attitude. Facilitative leaders don't inject themselves into the substance of debates. Rather, they withhold their personal opinions, guarding their neutrality

by being even-handed, carefully choosing their words, and carefully summarizing or enquiring into the different ideas under consideration. A neutral attitude helps the momentarily unpopular idea get a fair hearing.

Adherence to Process. The facilitative leader is assertive in matters of process. He or she helps the group frame the issues they will discuss and to identify key questions. He or she advocates for the team's norms or standards of professionalism. This includes each member's duty to listen attentively, to speak only when granted the floor, to keep their comments on topic, to keep the meeting on schedule, and to enforce parliamentary procedures (if used).

See chapter 4 for more on servant leadership.

Remember that committees are susceptible to groupthink. See chapter 4.

Desire for Consensus. Being responsible for the group's collective success, the facilitative leader has to be a consensus-builder. Groups can easily find themselves divided by competitive, win/lose situations. Facilitative leaders do not take sides but instead help the group find a consensus or win/win position. They also ensure that every stakeholder has a voice in the process, or at least, that the group considers the issue from all possible viewpoints.

Counterweight to the Status Arena. Committee members bring their egos and insecurities with them. Meetings are status arenas. Meetings might offer team members their only opportunity to gauge and improve their relative standing among their peers.[44] It is the facilitator's responsibility to be mindful of the jockeying for status and individuals' attempts to win while embarrassing a rival at the same time. The team-minded facilitator throws cold water onto the fires of status anxiety and promotes a sense of unity.

Status Arena
A meeting is an opportunity for individuals to assert their relative importance or social status. The facilitator's challenge is to suppress the clashing of personalities so that the group can have productive discussions.

FACILITATION TECHNIQUES

How does the facilitator provide for the smooth operation of the meeting in fulfillment of the objective-driven agenda? He or she actively manages the discussion. Among the many tools available for this endeavor are:

Ask open-ended questions. Push the members to go beyond one-dimensional answers by asking open-ended questions. For example, "What are some aspects of our recent field training that went well?" is superior to, "Did you like the field training?"

Ask for specificity in responses. Again, one advantage of committees is their ability to focus on detail. Do not be satisfied with generalities; challenge members to add specificity to their responses. For example, "How much time should be allotted to each component of the staff training?" is a question that probes deeper into a generalization such as, "We didn't have enough time for staff training."

Redirect questions to the group. Team members will instinctively turn to the facilitator or presiding official for answers to their questions. Instead of accepting that deference as an invitation to offer a personal opinion, redirect the question. "Cadet Curry asks a good question. Who has a perspective to share in response to it?"

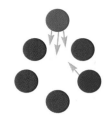

Redirecting a question to the group

Invite quiet members to join the discussion. As mentioned above, the facilitator works to evoke the best performance from each member of the team. Therefore, quiet members need to be drawn into the conversation. This is a delicate challenge because if the quiet person feels ambushed by the facilitator's pop-quiz style of questioning, the result will be counterproductive. A two-step effort is often effective. First, issue a general invitation: "Would anyone who has not yet spoken like to be heard on this issue?" If that approach is insufficient, when one speaker winds down, make eye contact with the quiet person, address him by name, and ask an open-ended question. "Cadet Curry, what are some points that have made sense to you so far?"

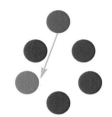

Using a direct question to bring a quiet person into the conversation.

Record ideas and make them visible to all. Flipcharts, whiteboards, and Word documents displayed by projector are good tools for capturing ideas. This approach accomplishes two things. First, it provides a written record of ideas that the group can refer back to and build upon. Second, it assures participants that each idea has been heard and considered.

Signal to dominating members their need to hold back. If one member begins to dominate the discussion by being the first to speak on every issue or speaking for the longest duration, the group's overall dynamic can suffer. Reel the member in without dismissing his contributions. "Cadet Curry has contributed a lot of ideas. Let's hear from some of you other cadets." Also, a subtle nonverbal cue such as an outstretched palm pushing air down to the ground – a gesture that signals "apply the brakes" – may help the verbose become aware of his behavior. Repositioning yourself to another section of the room, and/or directing your gaze toward others can also work.

Signaling for a dominate member to hold back so that others can speak.

Help rambling members wrap up. A rambling speaker, one who metaphorically chases his own tail during a long-winded monologue, discourages other participants from sharing their ideas. Wait for a natural pause in their remarks, then quickly interject a "Thank you," or more sympathetically, "Am I right that your central point is …?" If the rambler's comments touch on multiple subjects, an honest way to recapture the floor is, "Could we please hold off on those points for the moment because as you see on the agenda, we're going to examine those topics in depth later." Or, "Help those who are having trouble following you. In a single sentence, what is your main idea?"

See chapter 5 for practical tools for creative thinking.

Redirect the energy of combative members. The Core Value of Respect demands that we challenge ideas, not an individual's motives or dignity. Professionals assume that their colleagues are operating in good faith, unless proven guilty of misconduct. The unnecessarily combative participant should be reminded of those principles. "We're all on the same team. Let's try to work through the problem together." Other commonalities can be emphasized, too. "We all want the same thing, to support the new cadets." If the goals are in question, emphasize unity in another way. "We all seem to agree on the problem, so let's work together to find a solution." If the exchange is becoming heated and emotional, "Let's try to remain fact-based and hold back on the opinions." Finally, humor has a disarming effect, when delivered skillfully.

FUNDAMENTALS OF PARLIAMENTARY PROCEDURE

"Parliamentary procedure" is sometimes known as "Robert's Rules," after the popular handbook by that name.

OBJECTIVES:

17. Define the term "parliamentary procedure."
18. Defend the use of parliamentary procedure for committee meetings.
19. Define the terms "motion" and "quorum."

In a formal committee setting, the facilitator maintains order and leads through parliamentary procedure. Put simply, parliamentary procedure is "a code of rules and ethics for working together in groups."[45] These rules govern the "orderly and efficient transaction of business," and are designed to keep the committee or deliberative assembly running smoothly, whether it is in perfect harmony or in contentious debate.[46] Some basic (and very simplified) principles of parliamentary procedure are outlined below.

QUORUM & BASIC MEETING SEQUENCE

The Quorum. Basic fairness requires that a good number of members be present for the committee's work to be legitimate. A quorum of at least one-half of the group's members is usually required, but each group can set its own standard.

Order of Business. The chairperson calls the meeting to order. The first order of business is approval of the minutes. Then unfinished or "old" business is considered. New business - that is, matters that the group has not considered before - comes next. Finally, the meeting ends with adjournment.

Guidelines for New Business. Regarding new business, management experts consistently advise groups to consider only those items that were submitted in advance and added to the agenda. This ensures the items will be properly staffed (in large organizations), or at the very least, that all voting members will have the time needed to think about the idea. New business that arises "from the floor," without prior notice or coordination, is notorious for being slipshod. In the heat of the moment, the group is bound to overlook important factors bearing upon the issue. Only bona fide emergency matters should be considered from the floor.

Voting Format. Voice votes or simple hand-raising is the norm for casual and semi-formal groups. Elections of officers are always decided by secret ballot. Further, a secret ballot is required upon the request of just one member.

PROCESS for HANDLING MOTIONS

ASSEMBLY

1. A member makes the motion ("I move that ...")

2. Another member seconds the motion; he or she does not need to be recognized

3. The chair states the question "It is moved and seconded that (or 'to') ..."

CONSIDERING THE MOTION

1. Members debate the motion (unless undebatable), with the following preference in recognition:

   a. Member who made motion

   b. Member who has not spoken previously

   c. If possible, alternate for and against

2. Chair puts question to a vote "The question is on the adoption of..."

   "Those in favor of the motion, say aye (or stand, or mark ballots)."

   "Those opposed, say no (or stand, or mark ballots)."

3. Chair announces result of vote

   "The ayes have it and the motion is adopted."

   (or) "The nays have it and the motion is lost."

BASIC RULES FOR MOTIONS[47]

INTENTION	PHRASING	INTERRUPT?	REQUIRE A 2ND?	SUBJECT TO DEBATE?	CAN BE AMENDED?	VOTES NEEDED TO PASS?
To end the meeting	"I move to adjourn."	No	Yes	No	No	Majority
To take a break	"I move to recess for X minutes."	No	Yes	No	Yes	Majority
Put the issue aside for now	"I move to table…"	No	Yes	No	No	Majority
Send the issue to committee for further study	"I move to refer the issue to committee"	No	Yes	Yes	Yes	Majority
Propose a change to the basic idea	"I move to amend by…"	No	Yes	Yes	Yes	Majority
End debate (best handled by obvious consensus or by a pre-set time limit)	"I move the previous question…"	No	Yes	No	No	2/3
Vote on the main proposal	"I move the previous question…" *(For clarity, the chair states the final form of the proposal, as amended)*	No	Yes	Yes	Yes	Majority
Figure out the exact status of the motion and debate	"Parliamentary inquiry"	Yes, but only if urgent	No	No	No	No
Provide a tidbit of helpful information	"Point of information"	Yes, but only if urgent	No	No	No	No
Go back to an issue that had been tabled	"I move to take from the table…"	No	Yes	No	No	Majority
Break the usual rules and adopt a special one-time rule	"I move to suspend the rules which…"	No	Yes	No	No	2/3

HANDLING MOTIONS

The simplest way to conduct business is via unanimous consent. Under this arrangement, the chair simply leads and facilitates the meeting using his or her own good judgment. Individual members take as much time as they need to speak. Debate ends when everyone seems to be done. Basic fairness prevails. But when even a single member believes the matters are becoming too complex or contentious for such a casual manner, that individual may object. The objection brings all of the formal parliamentary procedures into effect.

motion. In parliamentary jargon, a formal proposal, beginning with the words "I move…"

MANAGEMENT

OBJECTIVE:

20.   Define the term "management."

Management is the practice of setting and achieving goals by exercising related functions: planning, organizing, leading, and controlling, through the use of resources (people, information, money, or materials).[48] Or to put it more simply, management is "working with or through other people to accomplish the objectives of both the organization and its members."[49] Management involves "taking charge," and accomplishing goals better, faster, and/or cheaper than the competition is able to do.

Do management and leadership share a lot in common? Yes. However, most scholars make a big distinction between the two fields. Management is "doing things right," while leadership is "doing the right thing."[50] Another helpful proverb is "managers manage things," while "leaders lead people."[51] But one thing management and leadership hold in common is that performance or accomplishment of the mission is the primary way we judge them.[52]

Fine Print: Management experts consider leadership almost as a subset of management. Notice that "leading" is one of the managerial functions. Leadership experts and the *Learn to Lead* textbooks, on the other hand, insist that leadership is a related, but unique field of study and practice in its own right.

Management Training
Even an in-ranks C/AB is a manager of sorts. New cadets are responsible for managing their personal goals, their time, their personal equipment, etc. Everyone is a manager in one manner or another.[54]

MANAGERS vs. LEADERS: *A Comparison*[53]

Managers	Leaders
Accept the status quo & work within it	Challenge the status quo
Administer	Innovate
Are a copy	Are the original
Maintain	Develop people, ideas, programs
Rely on control	Inspire trust
Ask, "How and when?"	Ask, "What and why?"
Keep an eye on the bottom line	Keep an eye on the horizon

MANAGEMENT & THE STAFF OFFICER

OBJECTIVE:

21.   Describe ways in which a staff officer is a manager.

If a staff officer is not in "command" of anyone, can a staff officer be a manager? Yes. Command over people is not the special characteristic that makes someone a manager. Rather, a manager is "someone who has responsibility for making a contribution."[55]

Consider three staff positions found in most squadrons: finance officer, transportation officer, and safety officer. Quite often each of these staffers works on his own. You do not typically find five assistant transportation officers, for example; theirs is an office of one. Consequently, staff officers might not have any supervisory duties – no underlings to "boss around." Yet each of these staff officers is a manager. The finance officer is responsible for contributing financial advice, for keeping track of the unit's money, for writing checks and making deposits, etc. The transportation officer manages the squadron's van, ensuring the oil gets changed on time and that the paperwork is in order. The safety officer is responsible for contributing safety expertise to the unit by analyzing safety data to spot trends, and planning workshops to help people learn about safety. If you are responsible for a program, an activity, or an administrative task that helps the organization, you are a manager even if you are not responsible for the work of other people.[56]

MANAGEMENT'S ETHICAL DIMENSION

OBJECTIVE:

22.   Defend the principle of ethical management.

Management involves people. Directly or indirectly, what is managed will have an effect upon people. That human connection means that management has an ethical dimension requiring managers to demonstrate integrity and respect human dignity. Dishonest, self-serving managers can bankrupt their firms, causing thousands of honest, hard-working people to lose their jobs while destroying the stock value that investors were relying upon.

The poster child for management ethics (or the lack thereof) is arguably Bernie Madoff. The manager of a large investment firm, Madoff was convicted of fraud, money-laundering, perjury, and other crimes in 2009 – crimes that directly relate to his managerial decisions. The *Wall Street Journal* went so far as to call him "evil."[57] For a term of 150 years, Mr. Madoff will manage an 8x10-foot federal prison cell. He also must pay $17 billion in restitution.

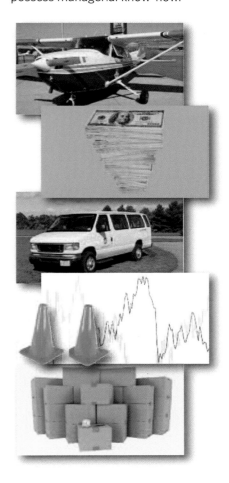

So Many Responsibilities
There are so many programs and resources to manage in a typical squadron. Staff officers must possess managerial know-how.

Managerial Decisions
Have Consequences
Bernie Madoff was convicted of crimes directly related to his managerial decisions. He is serving 150 years in federal prison.

According to the preeminent management thinker Peter Drucker, managers should focus upon their "responsibility and contribution," not their "power and authority."[58] A pair of experts put it this way: "We believe that a strong code of morality in any business is the first step toward its success. We believe that ethical managers are winning managers."[59] The ethical practice of management is important, Drucker says, because "none of our institutions could function without managers."[60]

FUNCTIONS OF MANAGEMENT

OBJECTIVES:
23. List the four functions of management.
24. Define each of the four functions of management.

Recall that we said management is "achieving goals by exercising related functions." What are the functions of management?

Planning is "the process of determining organizational goals and the means for achieving them."[61] What should we do? How will we do it? Who will do it? As planners, managers need to have a basic attitude of going about their business in a careful, systematic, purposeful way. The "I'll just wing it," or "I fly by the seat of my pants" approach is the opposite of planning. For example, it was not enough for the U.S. to decide to go to war in Iraq; an enormous planning effort was needed to figure out which troops, weapons, and supplies we would send halfway around the world, how and when they would ship, and who would bring them there. Because the planning function is the first task that a manager engages, it is not surprising that planning lays the groundwork for the next three managerial functions.

Organizing is "bringing together resources in the most effective way."[62] The resources include people, money, equipment, and the like. Managers organize by deciding how many people are needed to do the job, and what education and skills those people will need to bring to the team. Further, through the organizing function, managers divide the labor necessary for accomplishing the organization's goals. They create a hierarchical structure (or decide against one) that forms individuals into teams under the authority of supervisors. Therefore, it might be said that through the organizing function, managers decide where decisions will be made.[63] Consider the CAP search and rescue mission. Is it more efficient for each squadron to recruit, train, and equip its own ground and electronic search teams? Or is it more sensible for wings to pool their resources by creating just two or three teams, each comprised of qualified members from different squadrons in the same geographic area of the state? Whatever the answer, the basic question is a managerial one that extends from management's organizing function.

Fine Print: For our purposes we will consider management as having four main functions: planning, organizing, leading, and controlling. Some scholars use slightly different terms; some identify seven functions, others five; there is no firm consensus.[64] Nonetheless, the descriptions here represent mainstream views on the functions of management.

Planning for War
Before troops deploy overseas, an enormous planning effort must be undertaken.

The organizing function relates back to this chapter's section, "Organizations & The Staff Officer," pp. 55-57.

71

Leading, in its context as a management function, is "creating an atmosphere that will assist and motivate people to achieve the organization's objectives."[65] Through this function, managers "build and maintain a supportive environment."[66] From your study of *Learn to Lead*, you already know that leading involves inspiring and motivating people to achieve the team's goals, preferably by showing how personal goals align with team goals. Directing, coaching, supporting, and delegating are some of the tasks associated with this managerial function. Further, it is through the leading function that managers develop compensation (pay) systems, benefits, and other rewards to motivate people. The leading function is management's human side.

Controlling is the process of monitoring progress toward the organization's goals and making changes, as necessary.[67] Just because a manager has made a plan, organized resources, and led people does not mean that the team will reach its goals. Managers compare how the team is performing against the standard. Perhaps the people are not being motivated well. Perhaps the organizational structure is too unwieldy, thereby slowing the team down. Maybe the overall plan itself was poorly conceived. Through the controlling function, managers "prevent, identify, and correct deviations from guidelines."[68] The in-ranks uniform inspection is a classic example. Managers (the cadet staff) scrutinize the work of subordinates (cadet airmen) to compare the cadets' performance against the standard set by the *CAP Uniform Manual*. If the airmen look sharp, the managers know that the team is performing according to plan. If the uniforms are terrible, the more training, better motivation, tougher discipline, or a change of command is needed. Control is management's end function.

Quality Checks
Preflighting an aircraft and conducting a uniform inspection are examples of management's controlling function. In each, a manager compares performance against a standard.

PRACTICAL APPLICATION: PROJECT MANAGEMENT

OBJECTIVES:
25. Define the term "project."
26. Identify five key players in project management.

The most effective and meaningful way for cadet officers to learn about management is by actually managing a project. A project is "a set of coordinated activities, with a specific start and finish, pursuing a specific goal, with constraints on time, cost, and resources."[69]

By quarterbacking a bivouac, leadership academy, service project, or similar event, cadets learn project management fundamentals. This

Explore project management careers and certification programs through the Project Management Institute at pmi.org.

section discusses some of those fundamentals, but keep in mind that project management is a career field in its own right. When the Air Force wants to design and build a new fighter, for example, they will call upon certified project and program management professionals. Huge, complex, multi-million dollar projects can go wrong in myriad ways, leading to poor quality products and/or cost overruns. A project management credential provides some assurance that the project manager is a competent and capable professional.

THE KEY PEOPLE IN A PROJECT

Before examining the steps in the project management process, it will be useful to identify the key players.

The Project Sponsor is "the internal buyer for a project."[70] He or she is the executive-level leader who tasks the project manager with running the project, and/or approves that individual's request to launch the new initiative. In a cadet setting, the sponsor is typically the squadron commander or director of cadet programs.

The Project Manager is "the individual responsible for planning, coordinating, tracking, and reporting progress of a project."[71] He or she is the day-to-day leader who supervises the project team. In a cadet setting, this is the cadet commander, cadet activity director, or encampment cadet commander. The project manager answers to the project sponsor.

Assistant Project Managers are subordinate to the project manager and take ownership of a particular slice of the project. In a cadet setting, it is common to see one assistant charged with operations or academics and another charged with mission support or administration. In encampment jargon, these are the cadet deputy commander and cadet executive officer. Other cadet activities use the term deputy director for support, or deputy for operations, or something similar.

Stakeholders are people who have either a direct or indirect interest in the project. They have "something at stake." If cadets are conducting ground team training, for example, the wing emergency services staff is a stakeholder, even if they do not directly participate in the training event. If a squadron meets at a high school, the school principal is a stakeholder because he or she "owns" the building. As a matter of professional courtesy, the project sponsor and project manager need to coordinate their efforts with stakeholders so as to win their cooperation and maintain positive relationships with those friends over the long-term.

Customers are the most important people in the project environment. They are the people who directly benefit from or consume whatever the project creates. In a cadet setting, first-time attendees are the

THE PENTAGON'S PHOENIX PROJECT [72]

Imagine waking up one morning and learning that suddenly, without warning, the world's largest office building has to be rebuilt. That's what Pentagon officials realized after they overcame the profound grief of 9/11.

The attack essentially destroyed 400,000 square feet of space on the E, D, and C "rings" between "wedges" 1 and 2. What was the first thing the demolition workers did to launch the rebuilding effort? They took a break. In respect for that awful tragedy, a 30-day period of mourning was observed.

You might expect this complex project was destined to run over budget and over schedule. Military contracts are notorious for doing so. But not this time.

Hundreds of construction workers, engineers, truck drivers, heavy machine operators, and project managers got to work. A large countdown clock displayed the time remaining until September 11, 2002, the 1-year anniversary of the attack. On their own, the rank-and-file workers decided that they would finish a key portion of the job with mesmerizing speed – less than one year's time. Together the fiercely motivated crews beat even that self-imposed goal by 28 days.

Complex projects seem impossible to manage. With teamwork, determination, and focus, they can come in ahead of schedule and under budget.

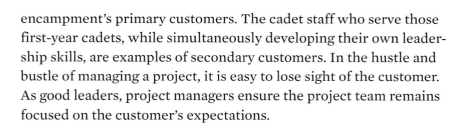

BOSTON'S BIG DIG: *A Project Management Nightmare*

Project management is easy and common sense, right? You simply make a big "To Do" list and get to work. Not exactly.

Even an average-size highway project might entail millions of individual tasks, many of which have to be completed in a certain sequence or require a special piece of equipment that may be in use elsewhere on the site. Add to that complexity a bazillion tiny details visible only to the worker on the ground. An entire project may grind to a halt for days because the metric lug nut does not fit the English bolt.

Case in point: Boston's Central Artery Tunnel Project. The "Big Dig" rerouted the Hub city's 3.5-mile central artery, the main highway running through the heart of Boston. Today, cars pass through a tunnel under where the highway once lay. Upon that old highway you'll now find a greenway or park. Also, the Big Dig connected the city to its airport via a tunnel running under Boston Harbor.

Keep in mind that while the Big Dig was underway, tens of thousands of motorists still needed to get around Boston every day. One journalist commented, "The project was so complex, it has been likened to performing open-heart surgery on a wide-awake patient.[73]"

Officially begun in 1982 and completed in 2007, the Big Dig remains the largest single highway project in U.S. history.

But this project is known for more than its size. The tunnels sprang thousands of leaks. Their ceilings collapsed, killing four people. One of the construction companies was indicted on criminal charges.

Massive projects are bound to run over budget and beyond schedule to some extent, but the Big Dig is in a class by itself. It took nine years just to break ground. Project managers and the government scaled back their ambitions a little, enabling them to finish the job *nine years late and $16 billion or 367% over budget*.[74] The Big Dig was a colossal failure in project management.

---

encampment's primary customers. The cadet staff who serve those first-year cadets, while simultaneously developing their own leadership skills, are examples of secondary customers. In the hustle and bustle of managing a project, it is easy to lose sight of the customer. As good leaders, project managers ensure the project team remains focused on the customer's expectations.

THE PROJECT LIFECYCLE

OBJECTIVES:

27. Recognize tasks in each of the four phases in the project lifecycle.
28. Identify five components of a project brief.
29. Define the term "opportunity cost."
30. Describe the five components of a Project Initiating Document.
31. List four checkpoints that can be used to monitor success during a project's Execution Phase.
32. Identify three elements in a project's Review & Concluding Phase.

Project managers approach their responsibilities methodically. They follow well-defined processes, document their work, and adhere to the technical standards of their profession. For our purposes, we will discuss a simplified four-step project lifecycle or way to go about managing a project. *

*Fine Print: To present project management fundamentals in a cadet-friendly manner, *Learn to Lead* describes an abridged version of the BERR Project Lifecycle used by the United Kingdom's Department for Business, Enterprise, and Regulatory Reform (BERR). Professionals will recognize BERR's similarity with the ADDIE (analyze, design, develop, implement, and evaluate) model.

THE PROJECT LIFECYCLE at a GLANCE

PROPOSAL PHASE

Someone suggests a good idea to someone who has authority to ok the project

The Project Brief

- Goal Statment

- Project Narrative

- Key Data

- Deliverables

- Action Recommended

PLANNING PHASE

The team decides how to accomplish the project's goals

Project Initiating Document

- Org Chart

- Gantt Chart

- Budget

- Governance Plan

- Comm Plan

Field Tests

EXECUTION PHASE

The team builds the product and delivers it to the customer

Controls:

- Staff meetings

-Inspections

- Schedules

- Budgets

REVIEW PHASE

The team reviews any feedback and closes-out the project

Feedback Instruments
Critiques, test scores, customer surveys, help desk requests, etc.

Recognition Programs
Customer loyalty programs, awards to project workers, etc.

Administrative Close-Out
Continuity file: all major documents in one place

TIME →

 **The Proposal Phase**

The first step in the project lifecycle is the proposal phase. Here, the individual who has a "good idea" makes a case for launching the project. He or she proposes the idea to the project sponsor via a project brief.

The project brief provides "an initial view of what the project is to achieve."[75] It is akin to a proposal; it is not a detailed plan explaining every task that will need to be done – that comes later. Put another way, a project brief is a strategic-level document. Some of the components of a project brief include:

See page 82 for a sample project brief.

Goal Statement: In a clear, direct sentence, simply answer, "What does the project aim to achieve?" Large-scale projects might include one over-arching goal supported by several objectives. In crafting goals and objectives, use the SMART goals approach. Goals need to be specific, measurable, achievable, relevant, and time bound.[76] (See the *Cadet Staff Handbook* for more on SMART goals.)

Project Narrative:[77] The narrative discusses the context of the project, explaining what is entailed and why the project is important. In crafting the narrative, set the stage by defining the situation in an insightful, coherent manner. Introduce dramatic conflict. Explain what challenges the organization is facing and how the proposed project answers those challenges. Finally, the narrative must reach resolution – the basic plan must explain how the organization can overcome the obstacles and "win." A narrative format makes readers privy to the author's thought processes, thereby providing context. In contrast, a mere bulleted list leaves unstated the critical assumptions about how the project works.

Key Data: Include relevant key data such as the project's duration, the estimated budget, number of people involved, location of project, etc. Each project is different, so the data needed to understand the project will differ, too.

Deliverables: List the deliverables – the clearly identifiable output of a project. These are the tools the project team must create to make the project run.

Action Recommended: Clearly identify the specific steps that the sponsor should take to authorize the project and get it started.

In reviewing the project brief, the sponsor compares the project's goals and benefits with the organization's long- and short-term goals. He or she asks, "Does the project represent a good idea?" "Does the project mesh well with the organization's overall plans?" "If we pursue this project, what is the opportunity cost? What other potential 'good thing' must we forego?" If the project makes good business sense, the project sponsor endorses the project brief, thereby authorizing the project manager to get to work on the project.

2 The Planning Phase

Armed with the sponsor's authorization to proceed, the project enters the planning phase and the project manager gets to work. During this phase, the team plans how they will accomplish the project's goals and objectives. They identify and obtain the resources needed to get the job done. Their plans become very specific because the project team develops schedules that show the deadlines for completing the project's tasks, and that work is assigned to specific people. Along the way, during this phase the team completes some deliverables that the customers will need later on.

Project Initiating Document. The key tool that the team produces during this phase is the Project Initiating Document (PID), which documents how the project will be managed.[78] It builds on the Project Brief by adding specificity and detail. The PID is similar to what the military calls an operations plan or "OpPlan." The PID is a file or binder containing all the plans, organizational charts, schedules, budgets, and the like that the team develops during the planning phase. Were the project manager to "get hit by a bus," a new project manager could step in, study the PID, and pick up where the first project manager left off. Some of the components of a strong PID include:[79]

PLANNING: The Critical Path to Warm, Gooey Cookies

The critical path is the longest chain of dependent activities in a plan. In project planning, the critical path is the major factor in getting the job finished on time.

For example, if it takes a minimum of 8 minutes to stir up some cookie dough from scratch, 15 minutes to bake the cookies, and 2 minutes to serve them, our snack will not be ready for at least 25 minutes. The critical path requires at least 25 minutes to complete – longer if you forget to preheat the oven, but never shorter than 25 minutes.

Of course, as we discussed in chapter 2, you also want to maximize uptime and minimize downtime. So while the cookies are baking, you clean up your mess and get the milk and napkins ready. By properly sequencing tasks that are not part of the critical path, you enable the project to be completed in the minimum amount of time, the time defined by the critical path.

Note. You may encounter the term "critical chain" in books about project management. That is a slightly different, more sophisticated method of project management,

opportunity cost. "The cost of an alternative that must be foregone in order to pursue a certain action. Put another way, the benefits you could have received by taking an alternative action."[80]

ADVICE FOR CADETS: *What's the secret in getting seniors to allow you to "run" the Cadet Program? Planning and communication. A cadet officer who presents the senior staff with a thorough Project Brief for their approval will win the senior members' trust and confidence. In turn, you'll earn the freedom to lead that you desire.*

PROJECT BRIEF: Wing Cadet NCO Academy

Goal: Prepare cadet NCOs to be effective leaders and mentors of new cadets.

Background. When cadets complete Phase I, they transition from "one who is cared for" to "one who cares for others." The Cadet Advisory Council believes that many cadets experience difficulty in making this transition. In our state, the squadrons are often small, so new NCOs might be the highest-ranking cadets in their unit. Lacking other NCOs or officers to be their role models, it's no surprise that new NCOs struggle. Therefore, it would be helpful if the Wing pooled its resources and offered a "Cadet NCO Academy." This weekend event would be part academic seminar, part hands-on skills training, and most of all, an inspirational experience for the new NCOs and the cadet cadre who train them. One of the Wing's goals for this year is to develop a better mentoring environment for new cadets. A Cadet NCO Academy would help realize that goal because we would be preparing NCOs to be the mentors we need them to be.

Eligibility: The Academy would be open to cadets between C/SrA and C/TSgt.

Leadership Team: The Wing DCP will appoint a senior member to serve as Activity Director. That senior member will then invite all cadet officers in the wing to apply for Cadet Commander.

Number of Participants. The CAC anticipates 20 to 30 students would attend. A student body that size would require 5 to 8 cadet staff and 4 to 6 senior member staff.

Dates & Location. The Cadet NCO Academy would be held at the State Military Reservation, preferably over Presidents' Day Weekend. Staff would arrive Friday night; cadet students arrive on Saturday morning. The program would conclude Sunday night, and everyone would depart for home on Monday morning.

Training Content: The cadet staff would develop a training plan. Possible activities include:

- Roles and Responsibilities of the NCO
- Leadership on the Drill Field
- Mentoring
- Constructive Discipline
- Professionalism
- Leadership in Core Values
- Leadership Reaction Course
- Leadership in Physical Fitness
- How-To Workshops: Inspections, the Demo-Perf Method, Team Leadership Problems
- Panel Discussion: NCOs from the Air National Guard

Budget: If the Wing authorizes a $500 subsidy, cadet tuition could be kept to $50 per cadet, inclusive of lodging, meals, and training expenses.

Deliverables:

- Training Plan that outlines each seminar, lecture, or training activity.
- Staff Plan including how we will recruit and select a cadet staff, and how we will parcel out the instructional and support staff duties.
- Training Schedule
- Budget
- Equipment List for individual participants
- Equipment List for the Academy as a whole
- Publicity Materials (for prospective students)
- Master Gantt Chart showing how we will manage the project's various tasks

Stakeholders. Mr. Wilson, the State Director, says that space on the military reservation is possible, if we work around the Guard's drill weekends. Captain Earhart, Wing Finance Officer, says that the Wing Cadet Account has the $500 necessary to support this project.

Timeline. This project would need to be approved by September 1, to allow time to select the staff and manage the various details, if we wish to conduct the school in February.

Cadet Advisory Council's Position: This proposal passed unanimously, 9-0.

Action Recommended.

1. Wing DCP approve this proposal, as outlined above.
2. Wing DCP appoint a senior member Activity Director ASAP.
3. Activity Director begin search for Cadet Commander ASAP, selecting one by 10 September.

Amelia Earhart
AMELIA EARHART, C/Capt, CAP
Chair, Cadet Advisory Council

"LIVE FROM NEW YORK, IT'S SATURDAY NIGHT!"

Lorne Michaels, executive producer of America's preeminent comic institution, Saturday Night Live, is known to say, "The show doesn't go on because it's ready; it goes on because it's 11:30."[81]

Reflecting on that reality, comedian Tina Fey, a former head writer at SNL and therefore something of a project manager, observes, "Improve every joke until the last possible second, and then you have to let it go."[82]

Project management requires a work ethic that is mindful of the unalterable, inevitable deadlines. The project team can work only so hard and for so long before the deadlines catch up. Santa departs on Christmas Eve, whether his elves are ready or not. SNL is on the air at 11:30. There's no fighting the clock.

Again, Tina Fey: "You have to let people see what you wrote. It will never be perfect, but perfect is overrated."[83] Cadets know that "perfect" is not a Core Value; attaining mere "excellence" is challenging enough. The principle applies to SNL and countless other projects.

An Organizational Chart that lists everyone involved with the project, their roles and responsibilities, and contact information.

A Gantt Chart showing when each deliverable must be completed, and who is responsible for getting the job done. Major resources are also reflected on the Gantt chart to show when they are tied-up or available. Think of it as a timeline view of the project, updated to show work that is completed and work remaining to be done.[84]

A Budget that shows the revenue that the project generates, alongside the expenses that the managers expect the project will incur.

A Governance Plan or a simple list of policies that identify how the project will be monitored and controlled. This document identifies who is authorized to spend money on the project, how much they can spend at a time, and how the purchases are to be made. It also would schedule times for the project manager to provide the sponsor with updates on the project's status, and/or identify milestones when the project manager must submit deliverables to the sponsor for approval.

A Communications Plan that details how the project team will communicate news to the potential customers, stakeholders, the press, or the public at large.

Field Tests. The final step in the planning phase is testing. The purpose of the test function is to demonstrate that the project output fulfills the customer's requirements.[85] In the software industry, before you "ship" the software, of course you will want to load it onto a handful of different computers and make sure it runs properly, working out

Gantt Charts help managers track the status of projects. What's done? What's left to do and by when? Just look at the Gantt chart.

Fine Print: Tests are sometimes called field tests, prototyping, dry runs, trials, or beta tests. We use the term field tests as a catch-all in considering the test function in general.

all the bugs. Not all projects are conducive to testing prior to implementation. (How do you field test a family picnic?) If the deliverables can be field tested, then test them. Field testing allows the project managers to check their deliverables in a safe setting, where they can make corrections before they place their professional reputations on the line.[86]

3 The Execution Phase

"No plan of operations extends with certainty beyond the first encounter with the enemy's main strength."[87]

FIELD MARSHAL HELMUTH VON MOLTKE, THE ELDER
PRUSSIAN ARMY, 19TH CENTURY

Put more simply, no plan survives contact with the enemy. Lt Col Jimmy Doolittle was forced to launch his squadron of B-25s 200 miles farther from Tokyo than originally planned.[88] Brig Gen Teddy Roosevelt Jr., was leading the D-Day assault on Utah Beach when he discovered his troops were landing one mile away from their planned target. Undeterred, he proclaimed, "We'll start the war from right here."[89] Proud of their ability to adapt quickly to changing situations, airmen are known to cite their proverb, "Flexibility is the key to airpower."

Flexibility is the Key to Airpower Circumstances forced Jimmy Doolittle to launch his raid on Tokyo 200 miles further south than planned. No plan survives contact with the enemy, and yet so much effort must be put into a project's planning phase.

Also, the Doolittle Raiders proved there's no subsitute for guts.

During the execution phase, the project team builds the product deliverables and presents them to the customer for acceptance. It is in the execution phase where the team implements the plan, conducts the operation, flies the mission, runs the event, or whatever the case may be.

Project outputs and deliverables add value only when they have been deployed or adopted.[90] They have to reach the customer. Steve Jobs famously expressed this principle as "real artists ship." It is not enough to have a nice schedule for a leadership academy; you have to actually teach some cadets. A new radar system might pass its flight tests, but it does not make a difference until installed throughout the fleet and put to work in the real world.

Controls During Execution. Because no plan survives contact with the enemy, project managers will need to create a process for monitoring the plan's execution. Someone must ensure that the improvised, adjusted plan finishes at the proper destination, on time, and on budget.[91] Project managers establish checkpoints – predetermined moments where the team asks, "What is going according to plan? What is not going according to plan? How do we need to react to fulfill the project's objectives?" Some examples of checkpoints include:

Staff Meetings: Each member of the project team verbally updates the team on how their slice of the project is coming along.

Inspections: Through a uniform inspection, a barracks inspection, or (in a manufacturing environment) a quality inspection, the project managers examine the deliverables to see if they meet the standards.

Schedules: By recording how much time was required to complete various tasks and comparing that data against the schedule (i.e., comparing reality against the ideal), the team manages their time and adjusts the remaining schedule accordingly.

Budgets: Managers keep an eye on the financial receipts, checking that the revenue they have anticipated is actually coming in, and likewise, they compare the expenses going out against the budget.

In responding to problems and changes during the execution phase, two practices are worth noting. First, managers typically prioritize the problems that their controls have spotted. Is the issue minor or mission critical? Obviously, mission critical problems take priority over cosmetic problems. Second, managers typically keep a log of problems, known issues, or bugs. Even if the team decides not to try to address those shortcomings during the hustle and bustle of the execution phase, if the project is ongoing or recurs annually (e.g., encampments), it is useful to capture those issues for future resolution.

 The Review & Concluding Phase

When the customer accepts the final deliverable or the project simply expires at closing time, the execution phase ends and the review and concluding phase begins. The goal of this phase is two-fold. The project manager closes out the project, while also collecting feedback and lessons learned to improve the project for next time. Some elements of this phase include the following:

Feedback Instruments. Course critiques, customer surveys, help desk logs, scores on final exams, and similar tools provide managers with feedback they can use to improve the project. Without feedback, how do you really know if the deliverable satisfied the customer? How can you be sure the project was as successful as you think it was? As mentioned in chapter 2, leaders need to fight for feedback. Therefore, all stakeholders (not simply the primary customers) should be asked to provide feedback. Not only that, the team has to systematically consider that feedback and decide what, if anything, can be adjusted to improve the project's effectiveness.

Recognition Programs. "A loyalty mindset," explains one expert on customer satisfaction, "...believes that investing in your customers will deliver return."[92] That return is reciprocal. "You first have to demonstrate your loyalty to your customers before they. . . give you their loyalty in return."[93]

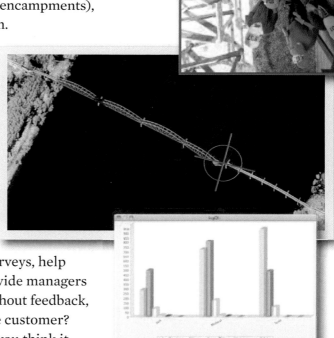

Feedback Instruments

Surveys measure customer satisfaction. Debriefs after a leadership reaction course enable the team to capture lessons learned. Bomb damage assessments confirm that your iron hit the target. Statistics and graphs analyze project performance from a mathematical perspective. One way or another, project managers need to check that they satisfied the customer.

In a environment like CAP, recognition programs are especially important because CAP volunteers are unpaid. Saying "thank you," presenting graduation certificates, and presenting awards and honors are critical tasks of any project's review and concluding phase. In the for-profit business world, customer loyalty programs (e.g., airline miles, hotel points, supermarket discount cards, etc.) deliver value even after the sale is completed.

Administrative Close-Out. During the review and concluding phase, the project manager administratively closes the project. This can entail recouping the project's supplies and returning them to inventory, preparing a financial report detailing all income and expenses, credentialing the project alumni and updating their personnel records to reflect their accomplishments, and other administrative tasks. Finally, a thorough project manager gathers the projects key documents – the project brief, the PID, feedback and critique forms, budget spreadsheets, a "lessons learned" summary, etc., into a single location known as the continuity file. The continuity file serves as a record of all major work that went into a project and provides a starting point for the next project manager if that project (or a similar endeavor) is ever conducted again.

STAFF COMMUNICATIONS

WRITING FOR THE BOSS

OBJECTIVES:
33. State the secret of writing effectively for the boss.
34. Defend the use of a staff package to receive formal project approval.

The boss often does not write his own material. The ideas are his but the words come from another's pen. Presidents have speechwriters, flag officers have their XOs, and business executives turn to marketing and communications specialists.

What is the secret to becoming an effective ghostwriter for the boss? It helps to have a close working relationship with him or her so that you not only know what basic message must be delivered in the letter, announcement, press release, etc., but have a sense for the various complexities framing the central issue. One of JFK's top lieutenants, Ted Sorensen discusses this point (see sidebar).

A great staffer who writes for the boss not only knows what the boss wants to say, but understands how he or she wants to say it.

COUNSELOR *to the* **PRESIDENT**

Ted Sorensen was not just JFK's speechwriter, his title was Counselor to the President and perhaps the greatest staffer ever to work in the West Wing. Sorensen explains:

I could listen to the arguments presented to [President Kennedy], assess which facts most impressed him in the Oval Office or Cabinet Room, hear the formulation of his conclusions, and then walk a few steps to my own office to put into words what I had just observed . . . Kennedy deeply believed everything I helped write for him, because my writing came from my knowledge of his beliefs. [94]

WRITING FOR THE WEB

OBJECTIVES:

35. Describe differences in writing for the web versus writing for print.
36. Identify seven tips for copywriting when writing for the web.
37. List four rules for formatting that can make web copy more reader-friendly.

The web is unlike any other venue, so a special approach is required when writing online copy. People go to the web to get information quickly. The audience is not in the mood for a leisurely, artfully crafted read. They browse; they don't read every word. Experts say that the typical web visitor gives a site just 3 seconds to grab their attention.[95] How do staffers write and structure copy for the web?[96]

copy: text created for the website visitor, consumer, or user

COPY WRITING

Place the key point right up front. Don't bury the lead. In chapter 8 we discussed the value of clear topic sentences. That principle is especially true on the web.

Limit paragraphs to just one idea each. This makes for short paragraphs. When copy is broken-up into bite-size chunks, it's easier to scan.

Choose simple, direct words. The *King James Bible* is famous for its beautiful, spare style. Notice how the translators chose mostly one- and two-syllable words in the well-known verse from *Ecclesiastes* (left). But also imagine how bureaucratic English might translate that passage, killing its readability (right).

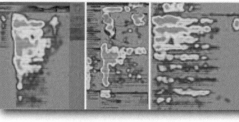

How We "Read" the Web

When you read a novel, you start on page 1, read every word, and move on to page 2.

On the Web, most people do not read, they scan. The image above is from an eye-tracking study. It shows that the upper left of the page receives the greatest attention, while the bottom right receives almost none. When writing for the Web, get to your point quickly!

KING JAMES BIBLE

I returned and saw under the sun, that the race is not to the swift, nor the battle to the strong, neither yet bread to the wise, nor yet riches to men of understanding, nor yet favour to men of skill; but time and chance happeneth to them all.[97]

ORWELL'S BUREAUCRAT

Objective considerations of contemporary phenomena compel the conclusion that success or failure in competitive activities exhibits no tendency to be commensurate with innate capacity, but that a considerable element of the unpredictable must invariably be taken into account.[98]

In a word, yuck!

Avoid jargon. Organizations are full of bizarre terms that apparently mean something to insiders, but are indecipherable to newcomers. Remember when you first joined CAP, how strange it all sounded?

Fine Print: This section on "Staff Communications" focuses on how staff officers present factual information about the organization on the Web. Blogging, slideshows, video, etc., are different animals.

"After the SAREX, I gotta get my ES training from the SQTR entered into OpsQuals on eServices. Next weekend I'm going to encampment training at Wing HQ and getting RST and ORM out of the way. They're required by 52-16, though the CAC is trying to get the NEC to change that."

Banish jargon from the web. Explain yourself clearly to newcomers.

Write short sentences. When writing a term paper, maybe you sometimes string out your sentences so you reach the assigned word count or page count. Not on the web. Be concise. Eliminate unnecessary words ~~that fail to add value to a sentence's key idea~~. Like that.

Respect the worldwide audience. The web speaks to the world. Not everyone is an American. Not everyone understands 21st century, middle-class teen culture. Slang expressions and figures of speech confuse people who come from a different background than your own.

Talk to your audience. Presume there is a "you," a reader. Tell that reader what he or she wants to know. Explain ideas in a simple, direct way, just as if you were casually telling a friend. Active voice is the key, so brush-up on the active versus passive distinction covered in chapter 8.

READER-FRIENDLY FORMATTING

If web readers mostly scan for information, how can you format your copy so they can quickly spot what they're searching for?

Use headings and subheadings. Notice how this textbook puts some headings in large, boldface, blue text, while certain subheadings are in regular-size but boldface black text. Having some kind of hierarchical system makes copy easier to scan.

Use bulleted and numbered lists. Readers zip through lists quicker than standard prose. If the sequence matters, use a numbered list. If the items in the list are related, but sequence or priority is unimportant, use bullets.

Highlight critical information. Make sure your readers notice important dates, fees, eligibility rules, etc. Likewise, if you have to phrase something in the negative, boldface the negative word. For example, "Bring 2 liters of water for the hike. Do **not** bring soda."

Write clear links. Use descriptive language in the hyperlink's text. For example, "To learn more about CAP, <u>visit a squadron</u> near you" is more informative and user-friendly than, "To learn more about CAP, visit a squadron near you. For the unit locator, <u>click here</u>."

BULLETS: FAST, BUT IMPRECISE

Remember that these guidelines about bulleted lists apply to the special needs of web copy. For serious work requiring intellectual depth, avoid bulleted lists because they leave critical information unspecified. A list can show only three logical relationships: sequence, priority, or simple membership in a set. Worst of all, the list displays only one relationship at a time.[99]

CONSIDER THIS:

Three goals, in no particular order
- Boost cadet membership by 10%
- Host ten cadet activities this year
- Improve morale

Three goals, ordered by priority or sequence
1. Host ten cadet activities this year
2. Boost cadet membership by 10%
3. Improve morale

What's going on in the bulleted and numbered lists above? We can't really be sure. Are the lists trying to say:

Activities > More cadets > Higher morale
Explanation: If we have more activities, more kids will want to join, and morale will go up. That sounds plausible.

or is the message:

High morale > More activities > More cadets
Explanation: If we boost morale, cadets will attend more activities, and we'll recruit more cadets. That sounds plausible, too, though it's an entirely different strategy from the previous one.

LESSON LEARNED:

Think of how much more intelligent and coherent a handful of simple sentences organized into a nice paragraph would be. Bulleted lists try to take a shortcut, sacrificing clarity and the writer's credibility in the process. Numbered and bulleted lists are okay for the web, but not for serious analysis.

CREATIVE LEADERS
GET THE MESSAGE OUT

Although this chapter emphasizes communication principles for staff officers in a workplace setting, remember that communicating still involves creative thinking. Recall the story of Admiral Jeremiah Denton. While a POW, he blinked Morse code to tell the U.S. he was being tortured (see chapter 5).

The poem below from WWII is equally clever. Nazis are occupying Norway. The king is in exile. The Norweigan Resistance wanted to send a message that would rally everyone around the king. That message is hidden in this poem. See if you can spot it.
Hint: Many Norwegians know how to read English.

Anropelse! [100]

Guddommelige forsyn bak ånders ledestjerner
Og gode makters lysdrift som fører folkeslag
Den dulgte vei fra mørke mot mål i fagre fjerner!

Skal vi var kjerne kjenne
Avmektig eller sterk
Ved det som her skal hende:
Et veldig vårens verk?

Til folkets indre styrke, dets marg og motstandsevne
Har vi vår lit å sette på prøvelsens dag:
En brist i sjelens troskap — og alt skal rakne, revne!

Kom, lyse fortidsminner
I diktning, liv og død:
Når nuets livsmot svinner,
Gi kraft og fremtidsråd!

Asker, 23 januar 1941
Ragnar Hauger

THE BRIEFING

OBJECTIVE:
38.   Recognize the two main types of briefings.

It is called the most exclusive document in the world. Each morning, intelligence officials deliver the President's Daily Brief (PDB), a 30-minute oral presentation that is accompanied by a 20-page, top secret analysis of raw intelligence pertaining to world events.[101] The PDB is the ultimate briefing. As a cadet staff officer, you will have plenty of opportunities to use briefings to express your ideas.

TYPES OF BRIEFINGS

A briefing is a succinct oral presentation. Although briefings vary in style, format, and tone, there are two main types: informational briefings and advocacy briefings.

Informational briefings provide the audience with information, without arguing for the organization to respond to that information in any particular manner. An overview of the Cadet Program, a "CAP 101" presentation, or a status update on a major project are examples of informational briefings.

The Ultimate Brief
An image of one of the few declassified President's Daily Briefings

Advocacy briefings provide the audience with information, while also arguing for the audience to interpret that information in a particular way. Advocacy briefings attempt to motivate the audience to act, to do something. An example of an advocacy briefing would include the CAC presenting to the commander a proposal for a cadet honor code, or a staff member approaching the local Red Cross and outlining a plan for how they and CAP can work together. However, advocacy briefings are not sales pitches that present the product only in its most favorable light. Good staff work and intellectual honesty require the briefer to address the proposal's weaknesses as well as its strengths. Briefers help the team make informed decisions.

ANATOMY OF A BRIEFING

OBJECTIVES:
39. Identify the three parts of a briefing.
40. Describe five logical patterns for grouping a briefing's main points.

In chapter 8, you learned that most documents are organized around three main parts: an introduction, a body, and a conclusion. That same basic structure applies to briefings as well.

Introduction. Greet your audience and explain your purpose. Who are you? Why are you delivering this briefing? What are you and your audience supposed to accomplish as a result of the briefing? Two examples are shown below.

> ***Intro for an Informational Briefing.*** Good morning. Most of you know that I'm Cadet John Curry, the encampment XO, and over the next fifteen minutes, I'll update you on the status of our encampment preparations. This will be your opportunity to redirect our efforts, if necessary, and be reassured that the cadet staff is on track to deliver a great encampment.

> ***Intro for an Advocacy Briefing.*** Good evening, I'm Cadet Hap Arnold, your CAC vice chairman. For the next ten minutes, I'll present the council's recommendation on how the wing can boost cadets' academic performance through an honor society program. I'll outline the case for an honor society; explain its goals, the award criteria, and how the program would operate; and briefly address some alternatives to an honor society that we considered but found unsuited for our wing. At the conclusion of this talk, we hope you will officially approve our honor society plans.

Body. The heart of the briefing is the body. This is where you present your main points. It is critical that the body be organized in a logical manner, but there are several ways to do that. Some logical patterns include:[102, 103]

A BRIEFING WITHOUT POWERPOINT?!?!

"[As the new president of IBM] one of the first meetings I asked for was a briefing on the state of the [mainframe computer] business. . ."

"[When the briefer was on his second PowerPoint slide] I stepped to the table and, as politely as I could, switched off the projector. After a long moment of awkward silence, I simply said, "Let's just talk about your business.""

"This episode had an unintended, but terribly powerful ripple effect. By that afternoon an email about my hitting the off button on the projector was crisscrossing the world. Talk about consternation! It was as if the President of the United States had banned the use of English at White House meetings."[104]

"Just talk about your business." Such simple but profound advice! A briefing is an exchange of information, not a demonstration of PowerPoint razzmatazz.

Cause & Effect:	What will happen if I do this? Cause and effect follows an action to its results. This pattern is useful when studying correlation or how two or more items are connected.
Example:	"We had to cancel the staff training workshop due to the blizzard. As a result, the cadet staff have not been told what we expect from them during encampment. Therefore, we need to either reschedule the workshop, conduct it over the web somehow, or find some other solution."
Chronological:	How is it done? What is the time sequence? This pattern is useful when describing a step-by-step process, or if working with a topic where the chronology of events is important.
Example:	"Cadets arrive between noon and 1400 hrs. Their first stop is the registration desk. There they meet their flight sergeant, who then takes them to the dorm. Next, the flight sergeant and tactical officer check that the cadet has all required equipment. Then . . ."
Compare & Contrast:	How are these items similar? How are they different? This pattern is useful when evaluating two or more items. The "pro and con" approach is a variation of this pattern.
Example:	In a career-focused activity such as E-Tech, cadets test out a handful of engineering career fields. Career-focused activities typically require cadets to complete some academic work. In contrast, at a leadership-focused activity such as Hawk Mountain Ranger School, cadets are busy with practical activities. They get their hands dirty and do a lot of physical training, but very little academics. Still, career-focused and leadership-focused activities are both "cadet friendly" experiences that are equally awesome in their own ways.
Climactic Order:	Which items in this set are most important? Least important? Which item occurs most frequently or least frequently? This pattern is useful when discussing priorities, or when the items occur in a hierarchical relationship.
Example:	The five main echelons in the chain of command are, in descending order, national commander, region commander, wing commander, group commander, and squadron commander.
Topical Order:	What are the items in the set? In the topical pattern, a group of items arises naturally; the items may relate somehow, but the chronology, sequence, or priority is not important. This pattern is useful when discussing the parts of a system, or in making a simple list.
Example:	The encampment equipment list includes requirements in the following areas: clothing, training materials, field gear, and personal items.

Closing. After presenting the briefing's main points, ask yourself, "So what?" to provide context and relevance, and "What happens next?" to ensure proper follow-through. A good briefing concludes with a quick summary, followed by answers to those two questions. Lastly, some presentation experts advise ending the talk with, "Are there any questions?" Others suggest that approach is not necessary because, one would hope, the audience and presenter have been engaging in a back-and-forth dialogue throughout the briefing.

Closing for an Informational Briefing. We're on track in all five key planning areas: staff selection, staff training, cadet training, scheduling, and logistics. The next step is for us to continue working on the cadet training plan, which we'll finish by June 1st. Our next opportunity to get together is May 1st at the actual staff training workshop.

Closing for an Advocacy Briefing. An honor society signals to cadets, parents, and the overall community that our Wing wants cadets to make success at school their top priority. The honor society can be a real motivator. Our detailed plan explains how we'd launch the honor society program, the award criteria, and the basic program operations. The CAC now asks you to approve the program and turn our plan over to the DCP, who is ready to implement it.

QUESTIONS & ANSWERS ("Q&A")

OBJECTIVE:

41. Recall five techniques for answering briefing questions effectively.

Successful briefers not only practice their core presentation, they prepare for their Q&A (questions and answers), too. One technique is to grab some index cards and upon each write down potential questions from your audience, then "rehearse" for Q&A by answering those potential questions aloud.

Four Possible Questions

• What is the toughest question you could be asked, the one that could destroy your main idea and challenge your credibility?

• What is the easiest question, the one you'll knock out of the park? How should you phrase your answer for maximum effect?

• Might your audience have a misunderstanding or wrong assumption about your topic? How will you gracefully correct that misunderstanding, if voiced during Q&A?

• What semi-relevant question might you be asked? How will you respond, while keeping the discussion on topic?

Q&A Challenges & Techniques

What are some tricks of the trade that enable you not only to survive but thrive during Q&A?

Rephrase for clarity. If asked a complex, meandering question, don't answer right away. Instead, restate the question in your own words. "If I understand you correctly, you're asking if cadets are required to join the military. Is that correct?"

THE STAFF PACKAGE

What, specifically, do you need to do to get the commander to formally approve your great idea? How do you win the okay for that squadron bivouac? For your Cadet Advisory Council idea to be officially enacted?

The answer is completed staff work. That is, you must ensure that every stakeholder has an opportunity to coordinate on and contribute their expertise to your proposal. Great ideas will die unless properly staffed.

If your proposal costs money, for example, and you do not coordinate with the finance officer, you risk the proposal being squashed at the last minute if finance says to the commander, "Sir, wait a minute, there's no budget for this."

Your main tool in coordinating a staff package is the staff summary sheet. Here's an example:

From:	NHQ Cadet Team	
To:	CAP/CC	
Subject:	ESS: National Character Day (FOR APPROVAL)	
CAP/DDR	coord	Lt Col Mayhew, Mar 11
CAP/CP	coord	Col Treadwell, Mar 11
CAP/HC	coord	Ch Col Woodard, 22 Apr 11
CAP/SU	coord	Col Guimond, 21 Mar 11
NHQ/EX	coord	Rowland, 22 Apr 11
CAP/CC	approve	

PURPOSE: Obtain CAP/CC approval to launch the "National Character Day" program.

BACKGROUND: National Character Day is a new wing-level activity that: (1) motivates cadets to take seriously issues of character and honor, while recommitting to the drug-free ethic; and (2) integrates the DDR program into CAP's overall Cadet Program.

DISCUSSION: National Character Day is a 1-day event where cadets learn the USAFA character development model, hear a character-affirming message from a distinguished speaker, and challenge themselves during a hands-on activity (e.g., ock walling, indoor skydiving, low ropes). HQ/DDR will provide funds, via reimbursement, to cover 80% of the cost of the "Character Challenge" portion of this event IAW CAPR 51-1.

RECOMMENDATION: CAP/CC approve the National Character Day via email reply.

CURT LAFOND
Deputy Director for Cadet Programs

Attachments
Tab 1.   National Character Day – Curriculum Guide
Tab 2.   National Character Day – Cadet Handbook
Tab 3.   National Character Day – CAP/CC Kickoff Letter

Answer one question at a time. If asked a multi-part question there is no harm in answering one part at a time, then following-up with, "Now what was the next part of your question again, please?..."

Be honest. If you don't know the answer to a question, don't try to bluff your way through it. In fact, saying, "I'm sorry, I don't know, that's beyond my range of expertise," can actually boost your credibility. If asked a highly-detailed question, you might reply, "I don't have the specific information you're looking for right now. May I get back to you on that later?"

Boomerang. A briefing should be a give-and-take between presenter and audience. If asked an opinionated question, one that suggests the questioner has an answer of her own already in mind, send that question right back, like a boomerang. "I'd like to know if you think the uniform is an important aspect of cadet life, or if uniforms are worn only by idiots." Reply: "It sounds like you have some strong views on that. Please, why don't you just share your perspective?"

Go offline. If briefing more than a handful of people, be sure your Q&A remains relevant to the group as a whole. Long, drawn-out questions that focus upon one person's particular question or problem, can be handled offline. "With your permission, could we take your question offline? We can meet right after this briefing and I'll be happy to give that question the attention it requires."

AUDIENCE FEEDBACK

OBJECTIVE:
42. Defend the need to monitor audience members for nonverbal feedback during briefings.

Monitor your audience for feedback. Are they agreeing with you? Challenging your idea? Personally offended by you for some reason? Becoming impatient? Presenters should monitor their audience for nonverbal feedback, the responses your audience sends by means other than words. Smiling, nodding, applauding, and a thumbs-up are positive examples of nonverbal feedback. Grimacing, shaking their heads back and forth, sitting with arms tightly crossed on their chests, rolling their eyes, etc., are forms of negative feedback. Many briefers can read nonverbal feedback easily enough. But how do you cope with someone shooting daggers at you with their intense stare? A four-star general shares this advice:

"We have to be confident enough in our people to listen to negative feedback and dissenting opinions, find the best way forward, and then lead in a positive direction. We all like the 'warm fuzzies' we get when people agree with our ideas and give us positive feedback. We naturally dislike the 'cold pricklies' that come when people

THE DISARMING HUMOR OF RONALD REAGAN

They called him the "Great Communicator" and the "Teflon President" to whom bad news just didn't stick. Ronald Reagan was a master at using humor to soften his critics and bring levity to anxious moments. Some of his greatest hits:[105]

In a debate, when asked if at age 73 he still had the stamina to serve:
"I will not make age an issue in this campaign. I am not going to exploit for political purposes my opponent's youth and inexperience."

At a press conference, when asked if he shared blame with his adversaries on Capitol Hill, the Democrats, he answered with a smile,
"Why yes, because for many years I was a Democrat."

Poking fun at himself for being the oldest president ever to serve:
"Jefferson said we should never judge a president by his age but by his work. Ever since he told me that..."

During a debate, when his opponent seemed to score points against him, with levity he responded,
"There you go again."

Just after the assignation attempt, while on the operating table, he said to his nurses and surgeons,
"I hope you're all Republicans."

His explanation for getting shot in the first place:
"I forgot to duck."

*disagree with us and point out our shortcomings. As leaders, **we have to be mature enough to deal with criticism** without punishing the source—the best leaders encourage frank feedback, especially when it is negative." [emphasis added]*[106]

TIME MANAGEMENT FOR BRIEFERS

OBJECTIVE:

43.   Comprehend the importance of time management while briefing.

In a face-to-face briefing, you are obviously taking up someone's time. Honor the commitment and be professional by staying within your allotted time. Moreover, have a back-up plan should you be given only half the time you had expected. What portions of your briefing can you shorten or jettison altogether? Especially when briefing an executive-level leader, be ready on time and end on time.

VISUAL AIDS & INFORMATION DISPLAYS

OBJECTIVES:

44.   List examples of how visual aids can be used to enrich presentations.
45.   Defend the idea that PowerPoint slides are not always the ideal communication medium.

What do you want the audience to think about? Are they analyzing a problem to find a solution? Simply absorbing some basic information that they can use later? Trying to picture how an event is supposed to operate? A visual aid, or more precisely, an information display, is a chart, graph, mapped picture, diagram, flowchart, whiteboard, or any visual tool that helps the audience think about the topic.

Cadet Super Chart

Here's the Cadet Program at a glance. Display the full chart as a poster or using a projector. Provide the audience with a small (11x17) version. "Show and tell" using the chart as a guide. It's a data-rich visual aid.

VISUALS TO AID IN THINKING

Visual aids can enrich a presentation. In the examples below, notice how data-rich charts and photos are used to help the audience think deeply about the topic. If the familiar, 1-page, data-rich "Cadet Super Chart" were converted to a list of words in PowerPoint format, at least 70 PowerPoint slides would be required to tell the same story.*

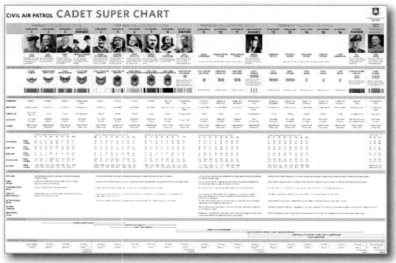

*The Harvard School of Public Health advises presenters to limit slides to 12 data points each. Edward Tufte criticized that standard, asserting that data-rich visuals are most useful. The "Cadet Super Chart" contains approximately 865 data points. According to Harvard's absurdly low standard, 72 slides (865 / 12 = 72.08) are required to present this data.[107]

The Uniform. Display a photo of a cadet properly wearing the uniform, or better still, use a cadet as a live model. "Show and tell" uniform rules and regulations by pointing to the cadet model or a photo projected on a screen.

Training Schedule. If briefing an audience on the encampment training schedule, for example, build the schedule using a spreadsheet (e.g., MS Excel). Show-and-tell using a hard copy of the schedule (one for each participant) and the electronic file via a projector. This method works for financials, too.

Airfoils. Find or make a "mapped picture" that shows a photo of a real airplane, with the various parts of the airfoil labeled directly on the image. Show and tell about the mapped picture using a projector.

Rules and Regulations. Present the regulation. Allow people to read them. Discuss the issues in open forum. Perhaps use a slide simply to visualize the question. Present case studies, in writing, as a means to discuss possible scenarios involving the regulation.

The Read Ahead. The simplest visual aid, and often the most effective, is good old-fashioned prose: clear sentences organized into cohesive paragraphs that build upon one another. Instead of verbally making point after point in a briefing, some experts advise briefers to write a carefully crafted 1- to 4-page statement rich with details about the subject at hand. The audience could read this thoughtful document in advance, or be granted a couple minutes at the start of the briefing. Then, the presenter could lead the audience through a "guided tour" of the document, or jump right to Q&A. The advantage of this approach, favored by Apple founder Steve Jobs, is that the bulk of the time reserved for the briefing is spent in lively discussion.

Respecting the audience means granting them access to all the information up front, versus making them endure one slide after another until you come around to the point that interests them. The result of enriching your briefings with information displays will be shorter briefings, more discussion, deeper understanding, and stronger relationships between the participants.

A GENIUS WHO PREFERED "JUST TO HASH THINGS OUT"

"One of the first things [Steve Jobs of Apple] did during the product review process was ban PowerPoints. 'I hate the way people use slide presentations instead of thinking,' Jobs later recalled. 'People would confront a problem by creating a presentation. I wanted them to engage, to hash things out at the table, rather than show a bunch of slides. People who know what they're talking about don't need PowerPoint.'"[108]

"The Height of Recklessness:" POWERPOINT GOES TO WAR

During the Global War on Terror, military planners increasingly made PowerPoint their means of communicating with subordinates. One author uncovered evidence that the PowerPoint approach was dumbing down the very serious business of fighting a war.

"General Tommy Franks [did not] issue clear orders that explicitly stated what he wanted done, how he wanted to do it, and why. Rather, Franks passed along PowerPoint briefing slides that he had shown to Rumsfeld . . .

[One of Franks' officers commented,] 'The way we do things nowadays is combatant commanders brief their products in PowerPoint up in Washington. . . In lieu of an order. . ., you get a set of PowerPoint slides. . . Nobody wants to plan against PowerPoint slides.'

"That reliance on slides rather than formal written orders seemed to some military professionals to capture the essence of Rumsfeld's amateurish approach to war planning. 'Here may be the clearest manifestation of [the Secretary's] contempt

for the accumulated wisdom of the military profession and of the assumption among forward thinkers that technology - above all information technology - has rendered obsolete the conventions traditionally governing the preparation and conduct of war,' commented retired Army Colonel [and professor of international relations] Andrew Bacevich.

"To imagine that PowerPoint slides can substitute for such means is really the height of recklessness."[109]

VISUALS THAT DUMB DOWN THE DISCUSSION

A briefing that relies upon PowerPoint can be successful, if done in just the right way. Correct? Not according to Prof. Edward Tufte (*Tuff-tee*). He learned that the engineers who were trying to analyze the Shuttle *Columbia's* situation while it was still aloft were made to communicate via PowerPoint, resulting in critical information not being transmitted clearly to top decision makers. Prof. Tufte scrutinized key slides and concluded that PowerPoint naturally distorts information. Slides can fool an audience.[110]

Annotated slide is from Edward R. Tufte, "The Cognitive Style of PowerPoint," 2nd ed., (Cheshire, CT: Graphics Press LLC, 2006), 9-10. Reprinted here with the author's permission.

The vigorous but vaguely quantitative words "significant" and "significantly" are used five times on this slide, with meanings ranging from "detectable in a perhaps irrelevant calibration case study" to "an amount of damage so that everyone dies" to "a difference of 640-fold." The five "significants" cannot refer to statistical significance, for no formal statistical analysis has been done.

Note the analysis is about *tile* penetration. But what about RCC penetration? As investigators later demonstrated, the foam did not hit the tiles on the wing surface, but instead the delicate reinforced-carbon–carbon (RCC) protecting the wing leading edge. Alert consumers should carefully watch how presenters delineate the *scope of their analysis,* a profound and sometimes decisive matter.

Slideville's low resolution and large type generate space-wasting typographic orphans, lonely words dangling on 4 separate lines:

Penetration   significantly   3cu. in   and velocity

The really vague pronoun reference "it" refers to *damage to the left wing,* which ultimately destroyed Columbia (although the slide here deals with tile, not RCC damage). Low-resolution presentation formats encourage vague references because there isn't enough space for specific and precise phrases.

The same unit of measurement for volume (cubic inches) is shown in a slightly different way every time

3cu. in   1920cu in   3 cu in

rather than in clear and tidy exponential form 1920 in³.

Shakiness in conventions for units of measurement should always provoke concern, as it does in grading the problem sets of sophomore engineering students.* PowerPoint is not good at math and science; here at NASA, engineers are using a presentation tool that apparently makes it difficult to write scientific notation. The pitch-style typography of PP is hopeless for science and engineering, yet this important analysis relied on PP. Technical articles are not published in PP; why then should PP be used for serious technical analysis, such as diagnosing the threat to Columbia?

A model to estimate damage to the tiles protecting flat surfaces of the wing

The Very-Big-Bullet phrase fragment does not seem to make sense. No other VBBs appear in the rest of the slide, so this VBB is not necessary.

Spray On Foam Insulation, a fragment of which caused the hole in the wing

---

Review of Test Data Indicates Conservatism for Tile Penetration

● **The existing SOFI on tile test data used to create Crater was reviewed along with STS-87 Southwest Research data**
  – Crater overpredicted penetration of tile coating **significantly**
    ◆ Initial penetration to described by normal velocity
      • Varies with volume/mass of projectile (e.g., 200ft/sec for 3cu. In)
    ◆ **Significant energy is required for the softer SOFI particle to penetrate the relatively hard tile coating**
      • Test results do show that it is possible at sufficient mass and velocity
    ◆ **Conversely, once tile is penetrated SOFI can cause significant damage**
      • Minor variations in total energy (above penetration level) can cause **significant** tile damage
  – **Flight condition is significantly outside of test database**
    • Volume of ramp is 1920cu in vs 3 cu in for test

(BOEING)

On this one Columbia slide, a PowerPoint festival of bureaucratic hyper-rationalism, 6 different levels of hierarchy are used to display, classify, and arrange 11 phrases:

Level 1   Title of Slide
Level 2   ● Very Big Bullet
Level 3   – big dash
Level 4   ◆ medium–small diamond
Level 5   • tiny bullet
Level 6   ( ) parentheses ending level 5

The analysis begins with the dreaded Executive Summary, with a conclusion presented as a headline: "Test Data Indicates Conservatism for Tile Penetration." This turns out to be unmerited reassurance. Executives, at least those who don't want to get fooled, had better read far beyond the title.

The "conservatism" concerns the *choice of models* used to predict damage. But why, after 112 flights, are foam-debris models being calibrated during a crisis? How can "conservatism" be inferred from a loose comparison of a spreadsheet model and some thin data? Divergent evidence means divergent evidence, not inferential security. Claims of analytic "conservatism" should be viewed with skepticism by presentation consumers. Such claims are often a rhetorical tactic that substitutes verbal fudge factors for quantitative assessments.

As the bullet points march on, the seemingly reassuring headline fades away. Lower-level bullets at the end of the slide undermine the executive summary. This third-level point notes that "Flight condition [that is, the debris hit on the Columbia] is significantly outside of test database." How far outside? The final bullet will tell us.

This fourth-level bullet concluding the slide reports that the debris hitting the Columbia is estimated to be 1920/3 = 640 times larger than data used in the tests of the model! The correct headline should be "Review of Test Data Indicates Irrelevance of Two Models." This is a powerful conclusion, indicating that pre-launch safety standards no longer hold. The original optimistic headline has been eviscerated by the lower-level bullets. Note how close attentive readings can help consumers of presentations evaluate the presenter's reasoning and credibility.

---

*The Columbia Accident Investigation Board (final report, p. 191) referred to this point about units of measurement: "While such inconsistencies might seem minor, in highly technical fields like aerospace engineering a misplaced decimal point or mistaken unit of measurement can easily engender inconsistencies and inaccuracies." The phrase "mistaken unit of measurement" is an unkind veiled reference to a government agency that had crashed $250 million of spacecraft into Mars because of a mix-up between metric and non-metric units of measurement.

Here "ramp" refers to foam debris (from the bipod ramp) that hit Columbia. Instead of the cryptic "Volume of ramp," say "estimated volume of foam debris that hit the wing." Such clarifying phrases, which may help upper level executives understand what is going on, are too long to fit on low-resolution bullet outline formats. PP demands a shorthand of acronyms, phrase fragments, clipped jargon, and vague pronoun references in order to get at least some information into the tight format.

PUBLIC SPEAKING DELIVERY SKILLS [111]

OBJECTIVE:

46. Describe ways to use body language effectively in presentations.

Your effectiveness as a speaker is directly related to your ability to invoke emotion and interest through the use of nonverbal communication. Your listeners judge you and your message based on what they see as well as what they hear.

In public speaking, your body can be an effective tool for adding emphasis and clarity to your words. It's also your most powerful instrument for convincing an audience of your sincerity, earnestness and enthusiasm. Whether your purpose is to inform, persuade, entertain, motivate or inspire, your body language and the personality you project must be appropriate to what you say.

As Ralph Waldo Emerson said, *"What you are speaks so loudly that I cannot hear what you say."* So be sure your appearance, posture, and attire is appropriate as well.

Here's how you can incorporate appropriate body language into your presentations:

Start with eye contact. Being prepared – having control of your message – is a prerequisite for being able to project and establish a bond with the audience. Don't just pass your gaze throughout the room; try to focus on individual listeners and create a bond with them by looking them directly in the eyes for five to 10 seconds.

Smile! There's nothing unprofessional about a smile.

Express emotion with your facial muscles. For inspiration, take a look at the *The Human Face*, a BBC documentary narrated by John Cleese of Monty Python fame.

Avoid distracting mannerisms. Have a friend watch as you practice to look for nervous expressions such as fidgeting, twitching, lip biting, key jingling, and hands in pockets or behind the back.

Tell a story. Highlight the action verbs and look for ways to act out one or more parts. Speaking about marathon running? Run a few steps.

Stay true to your personality. Don't copy gestures from a book or other speaker, but respond naturally to what you feel and say.

Make gestures convincing. Every hand gesture should be total body movement that starts from the shoulder – never from the elbow. Half-hearted gestures look artificial.

Vary your speaking position by moving from one spot on the stage to another. For example, walk to the other side of the stage as you move to a new topic or move toward the audience as you ask a question.

This section on Public Speaking Delivery Skills is from "Gestures: Get Moving!" reprinted here courtesy of Toastmasters International. See Toastmasters.org for more public speaking resources.

HOW TO OVERCOME NERVOUSNESS AS A PRESENTER

Rehearse. The practice will build your confidence.

Visualize success. If you see yourself succeed, you will.

Take a deep breath. It's okay to pause for a few moments to gather your thoughts.

If nervous, don't tell the audience! Just take a breath and continue as best as you can. Know that the audience wants you to succeed.

CONCLUSION

If you can understand the role and responsibility of a staff officer and develop your staffing abilities, you will stand out as an adult when you take an entry-level management position in an organization.

The dynamics of the staffer and boss relationship are a mystery to most young adults. But you know your role is to make the boss look good by taking ownership of one corner of the organization. You understand organizational structures, know how to manage projects (and have done so on several occasions as a cadet officer), and you'll excel where others flounder as a member of a committee. The briefing skills you study here and practice as a cadet officer will stay with you and quickly impress your superiors as they realize that yours is a well-ordered mind that grasps the big picture as well as the fine details. In this chapter, you've studied practical learning that will pay off for life.

NOTES

[1] Peter F. Drucker, *People and Performance: The Best of Peter Drucker on Management*, (New Delhi: Allied Publishers, 1997), 78.

[2] The Old Perfessor, Casey Stengel of the New York Yankees, http://www.caseystengel.com/quotes_by.htm, accessed November 2011.

[3] Bertie Charles Forbes, *Forbes*, vol. 82, 1954, via Google Books.

[4] Howard P. Greenwald, *Organizations: Management Without Control*, (Thousand Oaks, CA: Sage Publications, 2008), 6.

[5] Henry Mintzberg, "The Five Basic Parts of the Organization," *Classics of Organizational Theory*, 4th ed., Jay M. Shafritz & J. Steven Ott, eds., (Orlando: Harcourt Brace, 1996), 232.

[6] Ibid., 240.

[7] Elliott Jaques, "In Praise of Hierarchy," *Classics of Organizational Theory*, 4th ed., Jay M. Shafritz & J. Steven Ott, eds., (Orlando: Harcourt Brace, 1996), 247.

[8] Loc. cit.

[9] Hal G. Rainey, *Understanding & Managing Public Organizations*, 3rd ed., (San Francisco: Jossey-Bass, 2003), 28.

[10] Department of Defense, "Air Force Reorganizes Staff Structure," press release no. 082-06, (Washington DC: Jan 30, 2006).

[11] Oxford American Dictionary.

[12] Tom Peters, *Thriving on Chaos*, (New York: Perennial, 1987), 363.

[13] Exodus 18:18-23, NRSV.

[14] William J. Baumol & Alan S. Blinder, *Economics: Principles & Policy*, 11th ed., (Mason, OH: South-Western Cengage Learning), 142.

[15] Attributed to Robert Sobel in *Up the Organization*, Robert Townsend, (San Francisco: Jossey-Bass, 2007 ed.), 60.

[16] Peter F. Drucker, *Management*, Revised ed., (New York: Collins Business, 1973, 2008 ed.), 425.

[17] Drucker, 423.

[18] Ibid., 412.

[19] Ibid., 426.

[20] Steve Albini, "The Problem With Music," *Commodify Your Dissent: Salvos from* The Baffler, (New York: Norton, 1997), 176.

[21] Melissa Block, "Pomplamoose: Making a Living on YouTube," *All Things Considered*, (Washington: National Public Radio), April 11, 2010.

[22] Rosanne Badowski with Roger Gittines, *Managing Up: How to Forge an Effective Relationship with Those Above You*, foreword by Jack Welsh, (New York: Doubleday, 2003), 32ff.

[23] Amy Kates & Jay R. Galbraith, *Designing Your Organization*, (San Francisco: Jossey-Bass, 2007), 3.

[24] Drucker, 424.

[25] Ibid., 423.

[26] Ibid., 412.

[27] Kates & Galbraith, 25.

[28] Loc. cit.

[29] W.R. Ashby, *Design for a Brain*, (London: Chapman & Hall, 1965), 152.

[30] Kates & Galbraith, 23.

[31] Robert Frost, "A Masque of Reason," *The Poetry of Robert Frost*, (New York: Henry Holt & Co., 1979 ed.), 486.

[32] Attributed.

[33] Alex Kosseff, *AMC Guide to Outdoor Leadership*, (Boston: AMC Books, 2003), 222.

[34] Liz Robbins, "Miners Begin to Speak, Though Sparingly, of Ordeal, *The New York Times*, October 15, 2010.

[35] Attributed to Bearle at http://www.quoteland.com/author/Milton-Berle-Quotes/829, accessed November 2011.

[36] Antony Jay, "How to Run a Meeting," *Harvard Business Review Classics*, (Boston: Harvard Business Press, 1976, 2008 ed.), 21-22.

[37] Edward Tufte, *The Cognitive Style of Powerpoint*, 2nd ed., (Cheshire, CT: Graphics Press LLC, 2006), 30.

[38] Ingrid Bens, *Facilitating to Lead!*, (San Francisco: Jossey-Bass, 2006), 90-91.

[39] *The New York Times*, "Videoconferencing Etiquette," Sept 30, 2008.

[40] Bens, 9.

[41] Jay, 44.

[42] Ibid., 43.

[43] Bens, 46-49.

[44] Jay, 13.

[45] Jim Slaughter, "Introduction to Parliamentary Procedure," http://www.jimslaughter.com/parliamentaryprocedure1.htm, accessed October 2011.

[46] Henry M. Robert III, et al., *Robert's Rules of Order: Newly Revised*, 11th ed., (Philadelphia: Da Capo Press, 2011), 15.

[47] Slaughter, loc. cit.

[48] Warren R. Plunkett, et al., *Management: Meeting & Exceeding Customer Expectations*, 9th ed., (Mason, OH: Thomson South-Western, 2008), 5. [Note: We use a slightly modified version of Plunkett's definition.]

[49] Patrick J. Montana & Bruce H. Charnov, *Management*, 4th ed., (Hauppauge, NY: Barron's, 2008), 1.

[50] Warren Bennis & Burt Nanus, *Leaders: The Strategies for Taking Charge*, (New York: Harper Collins, 1985), 21.

[51] Attributed to Adm. Grace Hopper, USN.

[52] Peter F. Drucker, *Management*, revised ed., (New York: Harper Business, 2008), 11.

[53] Warren Bennis quoted in Cherie Carter-Scott, "The Differences between Leadership and Management," *Manage*, November 1994, 12.

[54] Ibid., 7.

[55] Kenneth H. Blanchard, et al., *Management of Organizational Behavior*, 7th ed., (Upper Saddle River, NJ: Prentice Hall, 1996), 7.

[56] Ibid., 5.

[57] Robert Frank & Amir Efrati, "'Evil' Madoff Gets 150 Years in Epic Fraud," *The Wall Street Journal*, June 30, 2009.

[58] Drucker, 6.

[59] Kenneth Blanchard & Norman Vincent Peale, *The Power of Ethical Management*, (New York: William Morrow, 1988), 7.

[60] Drucker, 2.

[61] Chuck Williams, *Management 5e*, [5th ed.], (Mason, OH: South-Western Cengage Learning, 2009), 8.

[62] Blanchard, 10.

[63] Williams, 9.

[64] Ibid., 8.

[65] Richard H. Thayer, ed., *Software Engineering Project Management*, 2nd ed., (Hoboken, NJ: Wiley / IEEE Computer Society Press), 2.

[66] Plunkett, 19.

[67] Williams, 11.

[68] Plunkett, 20.

[69] Sebastian Nokes, et al., *The Definitive Guide to Project Management*, (London: Prentice Hall/Financial Times, 2003), 222. [ISO 8402]

[70] Nokes, 223.

[71] Loc. cit.

[72] *The National 9/11 Pentagon Memorial*, "Phoenix Project Timeline," http://pentagonmemorial.org/learn/911-pentagon/pentagon-reconstruction-phoenix-project, accessed October 2011.

[73] Steve LeBlanc, "On Dec 31, It's Official: Boston's Big Dig Will Be Done," *Washington Post*, [via AP], Dec 26, 2007.

[74] Sean P. Murphy, "Big Dig's Red Ink Engulfs State," *Boston Globe*, July 17, 2008.

[75] BERR, Her Majesty's Department for Business, Enterprise & Regulatory Reform, "Guidelines for Managing Projects," (London: August 2007), 9.

[76] Ibid., 15.

[77] Gordon Shaw, et al., "Strategic Stories: How 3M Is Rewriting Business Planning," *Harvard Business Review*, May-June 1998.

[78] BERR, 22.

[79] Ibid., 22-23.

[80] Investopedia, "Opportunity Cost," http://www.investopedia.com/terms/o/opportunitycost.asp#axzz1cebije98, accessed October 2011.

[81] Tina Fey, *Bossypants*, (New York: Reagan Arthur Books, 2011), 122.

[82] Ibid., 122.

[83] Ibid., 123.

[84] Nokes, 222.

[85] Ibid., 169.

[86] Loc. cit.

[87] Original from Helmuth von Moltke, *Militarische Werke*, vol. 2, part 2; tr. Daniel J. Hughes.

[88] Tim Brady, ed., *The American Aviation Experience: A History*, (Carbondale, IL: Southern Illinois University Press, 2000), 201.

[89] Stephen E. Ambrose, *D-Day: June 6, 1944*, (New York: Simon & Schuster, 1994), 279.

[90] Nokes, 18.

[91] BERR, 36.

[92] Roger L. Brooks, *The Power of Loyalty*, (Binghamton, NY: Entrepreneur Press, 2010), 1.

[93] Ibid., 5.

[94] Ted Sorensen, *Counselor: A Life at the Edge of History*, (New York: Harper Perennial, 2008), 132.

[95] Chris Barr, et al., *The Yahoo! Style Guide*, (New York: St Martin's Press, 2010), 5.

[96] Ibid. Many of the basic principles discussed in this section are from *The Yahoo! Style Guide*.

[97] Eccl 9:11, KJV.

[98] George Orwell, "Politics and the English Language," *A Collection of Essays*, (Orlando: Houghton Mifflin, 1946, 1981 ed.), 163.

[99] Shaw et al.

[100] Ragnar Hauger, "Anropelse!," *Tidens Tegn* (tr: *Sign of the Times*, a liberal/democratic Norwegian magazine), 23 Jan 1941. { *Special thanks to Lt Col Becci Sundhagen, CAP, for translation services - CEL.*}

[101] Walter Pincus, "CIA to Cede President's Brief to Negroponte," *Washington Post*, Feb 19, 2005.

[102] John M. Lannon, *Technical Writing*, (New York: Longman, 1997), 254-257.

[103] Capital Community College, "Guide to Grammar & Writing," ttp://grammar.ccc.commnet.edu/grammar/composition/organization.htm, accessed October 2011.

[104] Louis V. Gerstner Jr., *Who Says Elephants Can't Dance? Inside IBM's Historic Turnaround*, (New York: Harper Collins, 2002), 43.

[105] From the compilation video, "The Humor of Ronald Reagan," posted by ReaganClub to YouTube.

[106] Stephen R. Lorenz, "Lorenz on Leadership: Part 3," *Air & Space Power Journal* XXIV, no. 3 (Fall 2010): 7.

[107] Tufte, 24.

[108] Walter Isaacson, *Steve Jobs*, (New York: Simon & Schuster, 2011), 337.

[109] Thomas E. Ricks, *Fiasco: The American Military Adventure in Iraq*, (New York: Penguin, 2006), 75.

[110] Tufte, 9-10.

[111] Toastmasters International, "Gestures: Get Moving!," http://www.toastmasters.org/MainMenuCategories/FreeResources/NeedHelpGivingaSpeech/TipsTechniques/GesturesGetMoving.aspx, accessed October 2011. Reprinted with permission.

PHOTOS & PERMISSIONS

All photos are from Civil Air Patrol or public domain sources, unless noted otherwise.

55 Scott Rogers via Google images

55 US Air Force Academy

57 Global Strike Command via Wikimedia Commons

57 5th Munitions Sq via US Air Force

57 13th Bomb Sq via Wikimedia Commons

57 Support Staff via Air Force Recruiting Service

57 325 Bomb Sq, U.S. Air Force photo by Airman Jason Burtona via Google images

57 B2 via Google images

59 Ferdinand Bol, "Moses and Jethro," c. 1655, Museum of the Academy of Arts, St. Petersburg, Russia

60 "Lakes of the Clouds Hut," via http://www.HikeTheWhites.com, under Creative Commons license

61 "Pomplamoose," courtesy of the artists, pomplamoose.com

64 "Project Runway," via Google images

65 White House photo via Wikimedia

65 Federal Reserve image by Ben Baker/Redux via Google images

65 Department of Defense photo via Wikimedia

69 Aircraft marshaller via Wikimedia Commons

69 Military Training Instructor via Google images

75 US Department of Justice, via Wikimedia

76 Military Sealift Command via Wikimedia Commons

76 Cargo loading a C5 via Flickr

78 US Department of Defense, via Wikimedia

79 "The Big Dig," by Ian Howard, via Wikimedia Commons under Creative Commons license

83 Gant Chart courtesy of GantChart Developers via Wikimedia under Creative Commons license

83 Visual Management Blog, http://www.xqa.com.ar/visualmanagement/tag/task-boards/ via Google images

84 Artist unknown, courtesy of Todd Joyce via The Official Website of the Doolittle Tokyo Raiders, http://www.doolittleraider.com/art_work.htm

85 US Department of Defense, bomb strike over Dunav River, Serbia

86 White House photo Time & Life Pictures via Google images

87 Uselt.com,

89 Map of Norway courtesy of Public Health Image Library http://phil.cdc.gov/phil/home.asp

89 Leather binder for the Presidential Daily Brief via Google images

89 Declassified memo: Central Intelligence Agency, via Wikimedia Commons

93 White House photo, via Wikimedia Commons

95 Steve Jobs: Wikimedia Commons under Creative Commons license

95 PowerPoint Ranger courtesy of Jim Placke nbc-links.com

96 Edward R. Tufte, "The Cognitive Style of PowerPoint," 2nd ed., (Cheshire, CT: Graphics Press LLC, 2006), 9-10.

97 Toastmasters International, toastmasters.org

CHAPTER 11
THE LEADER AS COMMANDER

COMMAND IS THE AUTHORITY to direct subordinates to perform duties toward the attainment of organizational objectives.[1] The notion of command presumes a military environment, where the command is established by and limited by law. If you believe that a commander is an all-powerful dictator, authorized to order the troops around as he pleases, you'd be wrong. In the western democracies at least, the age of tyrannical commanders has been dead for centuries. Therefore, command requires real leadership skill.

Former CAP cadet and Spaatz Award recipient Lt Gen Ted Bowlds USAF, (right), accepts the unit colors and assumes command of the Electronic Systems Center.

COMMAND RESPONSIBILITY

"You can't understand command until you've had it. It's the loneliest, most oppressive job in the whole world. It's a nightmare unless you're an ox."

Herman Wouk, *The Caine Mutiny*

The special challenges of command make it unlike any other leadership environment. Military commanders can fine and imprison troops who disobey them, and in wartime their orders could send troops to their deaths. With such awesome power comes awesome responsibility. What are some of the challenges and issues that frame command as an area of leadership?

PRIORITIES & GUIDELINES FOR THE NEW COMMANDER

OBJECTIVES:

1. Recall basic guidelines for a new commander.
2. Discuss priorities for the first 90-days of a command.

You're a new commander. What should you do? A respected Air Force study uncovered some basic priorities and guidelines that new commanders should heed.[2] Some highlights of the study include:

Stay away until you officially assume command. Incoming commanders distract the unit if they visit prior to the change of command, especially if not officially invited by the outgoing commander. Why? People will naturally want to meet the new boss, get a feel for her leadership style, and perhaps try to advance their own personal agendas. None of these effects helps the new boss take command when the time comes. Even more, the current, outgoing commander is made to appear an ineffective lame duck, and that's not good for the unit.[3] If the new commander is already assigned to the unit (i.e.: a promotion from within), she should be especially mindful of not appearing to undermine the current commander. Respect the commander by honoring his authority, which remains in effect until departure.

CHAPTER OUTLINE
In this chapter you will learn about:

CHAPTER GOALS

1. Discover leadership tools to combat the challenges a new commander will face.
2. Understand the role of the leader in setting and changing organizational culture.
3. Recognize the leader's need to measure performance of individuals and organizations.

Make a clean break with your old job. Don't try to serve in your new command role while also trying to finish old business.[4] This advice assumes the commander is in a full-time work setting, as in an Air Force operations officer being promoted to squadron commander on a different base. Geographical separation makes it nearly impossible to serve two units simultaneously. In a CAP or part-time volunteer environment, the principle may be less relevant because it is common for CAP officers to serve in multiple duty assignments. Simple necessity requires new CAP commanders to retain some of their previous responsibilities. Still, the underlying principle here is that command service requires a degree of concentration. A commander cannot lead with maximum effectiveness if he cannot devote his full attention to the responsibilities of command.

Prepare for new responsibilities. New commanders do their homework. When joining a new team, there is so much to learn. If charged with leading that team, the need to learn is that much more urgent. What is the unit's mission? Who are the key people on staff now and what are their backgrounds? How is the unit organized? What are some of the challenges facing the unit? What statistics are available to help you get a sense of the unit, its people, and its performance? Various command guides offer detailed checklists, but the essential point is that commanders should devote as much study and preparation to their command assignment as time permits, before assuming command. Some of these preparations are best made by talking with your soon-to-be new boss.

The Suits Are in Charge
For an example of the principle of civil control of the military, see chapter 3 on the feud between Gen. MacArthur and President Truman.

Command in the Civilian World
Metaphorically, the line managers of formal organizations, which we discussed in chapter 10, are something like civilian versions of military comanders. As you read this section on command, try to appreciate how the underlying principles apply to both the military and civilian settings.

YOU'RE ON TWO TEAMS
Suppose you command a unit. Therefore, you are a member of that team. Additionally, you, your commander, and your peers who command sibling units (e.g.: "sister squadrons") form a team as well. In effect, you're on two teams.

Commanders face a challenge of focus. They must keep their minds on the immediate needs of their own units, while simultaneously appreciating the bigger issues facing the teams led by their superiors.

THE FIRST 90 DAYS: PRIORITIES FOR THE NEW COMMANDER[5]

1. Understand your new position, your roles and responsibilities, and your boss's expectations.

2. Become proficient in your mission knowledge and technical expertise.

3. Get to know your people and their backgrounds, experience, capabilities, and aspirations.

4. Ascertain the health of the unit.

5. Learn how your team fits into the larger team's mission (i.e.: how a squadron contributes to the wing mission).

6. Determine the direction you want your unit to take under your command. Establish priorities for leading the unit to a higher level of performance.

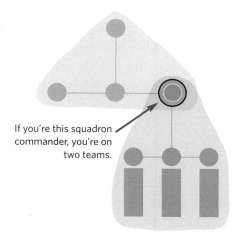

If you're this squadron commander, you're on two teams.

MOBY-DICK

Captain Ahab is a portrait of anti-leadership or command gone morally wrong.

For several days after leaving Nantucket, nothing above hatches was seen of Captain Ahab.[6] The mates regularly relieved each other at the watches, and for aught that could be seen to the contrary, they seemed to be the only commanders of the ship; only they sometimes issued from the cabin with orders so sudden and peremptory, that after all it was plain they but commanded vicariously. Yes, their supreme lord and dictator was there, though hitherto unseen by any eyes not permitted to penetrate into the now sacred retreat of the cabin.

Every time I ascended to the deck from my watches below, I instantly gazed aft to mark if any strange face were visible; for my first vague disquietude touching the unknown captain, now in the seclusion of the sea, became almost a perturbation.

It was one of those less lowering, but still grey and gloomy enough mornings, when that as I mounted to the deck at the call of the forenoon watch, so soon as I levelled my glance towards the stern, foreboding shivers ran over me. Reality outran apprehension; Captain Ahab stood upon his quarter-deck.

He looked like a man cut away from the stake, when the fire has overrunningly wasted all the limbs without consuming them, or taking away one particle from their compacted aged robustness. His whole high, broad form, seemed made of solid bronze, and shaped in an unalterable mould. Threading its way out from among his grey hairs, and continuing right down one side of his tawny scorched face and neck, till it disappeared in his clothing, you saw a slender rod-like mark, lividly whitish. It resembled that perpendicular seam sometimes made in the straight, lofty trunk of a great tree, when the upper lightning tearingly darts down it, and without wrenching a single twig, peels and grooves out the bark from top to bottom, ere running off into the soil, leaving the tree still greenly alive, but branded. Whether that mark was born with him, or whether it was the scar left by some desperate wound, no one could certainly say. By some tacit consent, throughout the voyage little or no allusion was made to it, especially by the mates. But once an old Gay-Head Indian among the crew superstitiously asserted that not till he was full forty years old did Ahab become that way branded, and then it came upon him, not in the fury of any mortal fray, but in an elemental strife at sea. If ever Captain Ahab should be tranquilly laid out - which might hardly come to pass - whoever should do that last office for the dead would find a birth-mark on him from crown to sole.

So powerfully did the whole grim aspect of Ahab affect me, and the livid brand which streaked it, that for the first few moments I hardly noted that not a little of this overbearing grimness was owing to the barbaric white leg upon which he partly stood. It had previously come to me that this ivory leg had at sea been fashioned from the polished bone of the sperm whale's jaw. "Aye, he was dismasted off Japan," said the old Gay-Head Indian once; "but like his dismasted craft, he shipped another mast without coming home for it. He has a quiver of 'em."

I was struck with the singular posture he maintained. Upon each side of the Pequod's quarter deck there was an auger hole, bored about half an inch or so, into the plank. His bone leg steadied in that hole; one arm elevated, and

holding by a shroud; Captain Ahab stood erect, looking straight out beyond the ship's ever-pitching prow. There was an infinity of firmest fortitude, a determinate unsurrenderable wilfulness, in the fixed and fearless, forward dedication of that glance. Not a word he spoke; nor did his officers say aught to him; though by all their minutest gestures and expressions, they plainly showed the uneasy, if not painful, consciousness of being under a troubled master-eye. And not only that, but moody stricken Ahab stood before them with a crucifixion in his face; in all the nameless regal overbearing dignity of some mighty woe.

Ere long, from his first visit in the air, he withdrew into his cabin. But after that morning, he was every day visible to the crew; either standing in his pivot-hole, or seated upon an ivory stool he had; or heavily walking the

Adam Hunter Peck

deck. He became still less and less a recluse, but he seemed as unnecessary there as another mast. Nearly all whaling preparatives needing supervision the mates were fully competent to, so that there was little or nothing, out of himself, to employ or excite Ahab, now.

Nevertheless, even the barest, ruggedest, most thundercloven old oak will at least send forth some few green sprouts. More than once did he put forth the faint blossom of a look, which, in any other man, would have soon flowered out in a smile.

Among sea-commanders, the old greybeards will oftenest leave their berths to visit the night-cloaked deck. It was so with Ahab; only that now, of late, he seemed so much to live in the open air, that truly speaking, his visits were more to the cabin, than from, the cabin to the planks. "It feels like going down into one's tomb," - he would mutter to himself, - "for an old captain like me to be descending this narrow scuttle, to go to my grave-dug berth."

So, almost every twenty-four hours, when the watches of the night were set, when this sort of steady quietude would begin to prevail, ere long the old man would emerge, griping at the iron banister, to help his crippled way. Some considerating touch of humanity was in him; for at times like these, he usually abstained from patrolling the quarter-deck; because to his wearied mates, seeking repose within six inches of his ivory heel, such would have been the reverberating crack and din of that bony step, that their dreams would have been of the crunching teeth of sharks.

Stubb, the odd second mate, came up from below, and with a certain unassured, deprecating humorousness, hinted that if Captain Ahab was pleased to walk the planks, then, no one could say nay; but there might be some way of muffling the noise; hinting something indistinctly and hesitatingly about a globe of tow, and the insertion into it, of the ivory heel. Ah! Stubb, thou did'st not know Ahab then.

"Am I a cannon-ball, Stubb," said Ahab, "that thou wouldst wad me that fashion? But go thy ways; I had forgot. Below to thy nightly grave; where such as ye sleep between shrouds, to use ye to the filling one at last. - Down, dog, and kennel!"

Starting at the unforeseen concluding exclamation of the so suddenly scornful old man, Stubb was speechless a moment; then said excitedly, "I am not used to be spoken to that way, sir; I do but less than half like it, sir."

"Avast!" gritted Ahab between his set teeth, and violently moving away, as if to avoid some passionate temptation.

"No, sir; not yet," said Stubb, emboldened, "I will not tamely be called a dog, sir."

"Then be called ten times a donkey, and a mule, and an ass, and begone, or I'll clear the world of thee!"

As he said this, Ahab advanced upon him with such overbearing terrors in his aspect, that Stubb involuntarily retreated.

"I was never served so before without giving a hard blow for it," muttered Stubb, as he found himself descending the cabin-scuttle.

"It's very queer. How he flashed at me! - his eyes like powder-pans! is he mad? He might as well have kicked me, and done with it. Maybe he did kick me, and I didn't observe it, I was so taken all aback with his brow, somehow. It flashed like a bleached bone."

When Stubb had departed, Ahab stood for a while leaning over the bulwarks; and then, as had been usual with him of late, calling a sailor of the watch, he sent him below for his ivory stool, and also his pipe. Lighting the pipe at the binnacle lamp and planting the stool on the weather side of the deck, he sat and smoked.

In old Norse times, the thrones of the sea-loving Danish kings were fabricated, saith tradition, of the tusks of the Narwhale. How could one look at Ahab then, seated on that tripod of bones, without bethinking him of the royalty it symbolized? For a Khan of the plank, and a king of the sea, and a great lord of Leviathans was Ahab . . .

Condensed from Herman Melville's **MOBY-DICK**, chapters XXVIII through XXX

PERSONAL CHALLENGES FOR NEW COMMANDERS

"Beware of all enterprises that require new clothes."

Henry David Thoreau, *Walden*[7]

When assuming command of an organization, it's natural to have some fears about the challenges you will face. This section identifies some common pitfalls for new commanders to watch out for as they assume the top leadership role.

OBJECTIVES:

3. Identify three challenges a new commander may face when assuming command.

Be Yourself. People are not just hired; their individual judgment is hired, too. New commanders may feel that they need to transform their personality or fundamentally become someone else upon taking command. The experts say don't. "Don't change – you wouldn't be in command if you didn't deserve it."[8] Or to paraphrase Thoreau, a self-confident commander does not don new clothes.

You're not one of "the guys" anymore. "The very nature of command separates you from everyone else."[9] It's lonely at the top. Even if you had some supervisory responsibilities before becoming a commander, you now are officially authorized to hire and fire, discipline and reprimand, affect people's pay, reassign people to new duties, alter the basic way the unit does business, decide who wins certain awards, and referee interpersonal squabbles. "With power, you will be surprised by just how much silent scrutiny is focused upon you," confesses one first-time manager. "You won't notice it at first."[10] A new boss will find that he is suddenly excluded from the old group, or in the very least, that relationships with old peers somehow become different.

Beware the temptations of ego. A major challenge that new commanders or first-time leaders face is the temptation to wield their newfound power.[11] A new boss asks for something, and it is done. They direct people, and "Hey look at that! The troops do as I ask." Power can be intoxicating, and its abuse is a sign of immaturity. Moreover, the "rank has its privileges" mindset is contrary to the principles of servant leadership. "Rank does not confer privilege or give power. It imposes responsibility."[12] Being in charge means you

KING GEORGE I

Perhaps you've heard that upon completing two tremendously successful terms as our first president, George Washington was offered a crown, but selflessly turned it down.

Charming as it is, the myth is false. In May of 1782, seven years before Washington was first elected president, an obscure army colonel fancifully suggested that Washington start a new country to the west of the United States, and install himself as king there. The reign of George I was simply one bystander's half-baked idea, and Washington immediately dismissed it. But like all good stories, this one took on a life of its own, and eventually lost all resemblance to the truth.[13]

But for aspiring leaders, the facts do not get in the way of the lesson. The mythical story of Washington rejecting a crown illustrates Americans' desire for selfless leaders. The myth demonstrates an American philosophy of leadership. Leaders have a job to do, and they shouldn't busy themselves by seeking special perks that aggrandize them. Egotism is a sin for American leaders; humility is a virtue. Washington was offered no crown, but his lesson of humility is nevertheless worthwhile.

John Trumbull, *Washington Resigning His Commission* (detail)

THE PRESTIGE, PRIVILEGE & THE BURDEN OF COMMAND

The meditation below considers the challenges that naval skippers face on the high seas, but the overall theme is a useful illustration of the unique responsibilities of command.

Only a seaman realizes to what extent an entire ship reflects the personality and ability of one individual, her Commanding Officer. To a landsman this is not understandable, and sometimes it is even difficult for us to comprehend, but it is so. A ship at sea is a distant world in herself and in consideration of the protracted and distant operations of the fleet units the Navy must place great power, responsibility and trust in the hands of those leaders chosen for command.

In each ship there is one man who, in the hour of emergency or peril at sea, can turn to no other man. There is one who alone is ultimately responsible for the safe navigation, engineering performance, accurate gunfiring and morale of his ship. He is the Commanding Officer. He is the ship.

This is the most difficult and demanding assignment in the Navy. There is not an instant during his tour of duty as Commanding Officer that he can escape the grasp of command responsibility. His privileges in view of his obligations are most ludicrously small; nevertheless command is the spur which has given the Navy its great leaders.

It is a duty which most richly deserves the highest, time-honored title of the seafaring world: "CAPTAIN."[14]

are responsible for helping subordinates excel; you serve their needs. A true servant will not become drunk with power. One Air Force chief master sergeant felt so strongly about this principle that he wrote a book for new lieutenants on the topic. Consider the chief's point of view:

For more on servant leadership, see chapter 3.

> *Yeah, you're the lieutenant. At least in your mind, you're the boss. Get over it! You're still accountable, but you're not going to succeed unless your troops become your disciples. If you're cocky and try to impress them with your authority, you'll quickly find how lonely it can be at the top . . . If you're [in command] to get promoted, watch out! Your troops will sense that in eight seconds and will make life hell for you.*[15]

Misuse of power results in subordinates, peers, and superiors questioning the new commander's readiness to lead.[16] One simple preventive measure is for new leaders to remind themselves of servant leadership principles.

LEADING THROUGH A COMMAND INTENT

OBJECTIVES:

4.   Describe the steps in developing a command intent.
5.   List and briefly define the components of a command intent.
6.   Recall three approaches for communicating command intent.

Commander's intent, as we learned in chapter 4, is the leader's concise expression of purpose.[17] It is the lens through which followers view their individual jobs, make decisions regarding how they will contribute to the team's overall effort, and react to unforeseen challenges. Command intent provides at least a hint of a right response when a follower meets the unexpected. How do you develop a commander's intent? Communicate it? Work with others towards it?

Developing a Command Intent. The starting point for developing your command intent is the command intent you receive from *your* commander. Command intent at one echelon – say a squadron – must be consistent with the command intent of the higher echelon – the group or wing.[18] Second, the mission at hand will specify goals or objectives, of course, but command intent takes that mission synopsis a step further. It provides the *why,* the context for the mission that informs troops in the field as they use their best judgment in responding to changing circumstances. Therefore, command intent should include an assessment of what the opposition is trying to do and why your team is working against that aim.[19] Further, command intent should address the scope of authority that troops are empowered to exercise in the field. What types of decisions are prudent for them to make on their own, and what problems are so sizable that the decision ought to be elevated and made at a higher level? Command intent offers a view toward what types of risks are acceptable in pursuing the mission, and what types of risks are so potentially catastrophic as to send the mission back to the drawing board.[20]

Communicating a Command Intent. How do you make your command intent known to your subordinates? Because leadership is an art, there are several potential "right" answers to this question.

The most formal approach is via a carefully prepared speech or written document. Executive-level leaders (e.g.: generals, presidents) often select this method because the challenges facing their teams are so complex that an offhand remark can send unintended messages. A written document has the advantage of staying power – people can refer back to it later. Either way, top-level leaders see the need to deliver a precise message.

A NEED FOR COMMAND INTENT

You're an Air Force combat controller deployed with Army infantry. Your team has been ordered to take a bridge, but when you arrive on scene, you see that the enemy has already destroyed it.

What do you do now? Should you hold and wait for your rear echelon to arrive, while defending the general area? Advance into the town to look for bad guys? Pursue a secondary objective? Call for instructions?

An order to merely "take the bridge" is insufficient. The leaders and troops on-scene need the fuller picture that command intent provides.

A second approach involves the commander making informal remarks and simply talking through the situation and its challenges, perhaps even encouraging subordinate leaders to ask questions and engage in a give-and-take dialogue. A respected Navy text recommends skippers use the ship public address system each morning to communicate the command philosophy for that day's operations.[21]

A third method is suited to leaders who are weak communicators. Simply allow the passage of time to reveal your overall philosophies, expectations, and intentions.[22] Communicate intent via simple example, trusting that actions speak louder than words. This final approach is unsuited to complex missions and situations where time is critical.

Cooperate & Imagine an Intent. Complex problems cannot be solved by a single team. A coalition of teams is needed. When multiple teams from different agencies, different military units, or different nations come together, it is possible that no single person will possess command and control authority.

Consider the Haitian earthquake of 2010. Haiti was already one of the most impoverished and least self-sustaining nations on earth. A 7.0 quake crippled Haiti, killing over 300,000 people by some estimates.[23] Fortunately, the world community came to the rescue. Iceland, China, and Israel sent help, in addition to Haiti's neighbor the Dominican Republic and of course the United States as the closest superpower. Who was in charge? No one really. Chaos reigned. One expert explains, "In many people's minds, command and leadership come together in one person. In practice, that is not always the case."[24]

Even if the commander's chair is vacant, the need for intent remains. It's up to the participants to figure out what that intent should be.

> "Command intent is a reflection of a collective rather than an individual . . . Command intent is consistent with unity of purpose without the requirement for a single authority or unity of command. Using only the word *intent* [versus *commander's intent*] is best because it does not assume the origins of intent and hence allows one to focus on the function of intent. . . Intent is an expression of purpose. As such, the appropriateness of the purpose is a legitimate subject for deliberation."[25]

In other words, command intent is not always explicit. Different teams might imagine the intent in differently. Therefore, leaders who recognize the need for command intent work with their counterparts to build a consensus for a workable understanding of intent. Even without a commander, intent can be conceived.

COMPONENTS OF A COMMAND INTENT

- A basic philosophy that is consistent with the superior commander's own command intent

- An explanation of the why of the mission matters

- An assessment of what the opposition is trying to do

- An assessment of the risks that the troops are likely to encounter

- A scope of empowerment – the scope of issues that troops are empowered to settle on their own judgment and the scope of matters that should be decided at a higher level

- A tolerance for risk and a sense of when the risks outweigh potential benefits

Who's the Boss?
Two Brazilian officers operating under UN auspices confer with a US officer and a local civilian official during relief efforts following the 2010 quake in Haiti.

DEVELOPING THE MISSION STATEMENT

"If you don't know where you're going, you might not get there."[26]

Yogi Berra, baseball player & philosopher

OBJECTIVES:

7.   Identify the components of a mission statement.
8.   Describe the steps in developing a mission statement.

As we learned in chapter 3, the mission is the reason why the team exists.[27] Organizations carefully craft the expression of their mission. Done well, a mission statement inspires the team, defines what the organization does, and lays the foundation for a positive organizational culture.[28] The process of defining a mission and articulating a vision is the central function of leadership.[29] What goes into an effective mission statement? How do leaders go about crafting them?

Fine Print: Some organizations craft two statements, one defining the mission and another expressing a vision. A vision statement is the organization's "future picture," which we described in chapters 2 and 5. For our purposes here, we'll focus upon the mission statement and not dwell on the distinction between mission and vision.

Components of a Mission Statement

An Overarching Reason for Being. The mission of a business is to make money. A bomb squadron's mission is to drop bombs. End of story, right? Experts say that mission statements require a lot more specificity. If the mission is too abstract, it won't click with the team members. Therefore, a mission statement should offer an overarching reason for being. It ought to answer in a high-minded way the question, "Why are we here?"[30] Consider how Northrop Grumman, maker of the F-35 and *Global Hawk* UAV, explains itself:

> "Our vision is to be the most trusted provider of systems and technologies that ensure the security and freedom of our nation and its allies. As the technology leader, we will define the future of defense—from undersea to outer space, and in cyberspace."[31]

Such a well-rounded mission statement gives a full sense of why the company exists. Northrop Grumman's approach is so much more nuanced and informative than a possible alternative: "Make money by building weapons." Next, consider how the USAF Honor Guard perceives itself:

> "The mission of the U.S. Air Force Honor Guard is to represent Airmen to the American Public and the World. The vision of the USAF Honor Guard is to ensure a legacy of Airmen who:
>
> >   PROMOTE the Mission...
> >   PROTECT the Standards...
> >   PERFECT the Image...
> >   PRESERVE the Heritage."[32]

If you thought the Air Force Honor Guard was merely a drill team, albeit a fancy one, you'd be wrong. Drill is what they do, but their business is the much broader task of representing airmen to the world and exemplifying the best traditions of the service. Taken together, their mission and vision statements offer a concise, but thorough, explanation of why the Air Force has an honor guard.

CAP MISSION STATEMENT

To serve America by performing Homeland Security and humanitarian missions for communities, states, and nation; developing our country's youth; and educating our citizens on the importance of air and space power.

CAP VISION STATEMENT

America's Air Force Auxiliary, Civil Air Patrol, building the nation's finest force of citizen volunteers-performing Missions for America.

CADET PROGRAMS MISSION STATEMENT

The Cadet Program transforms youth into dynamic Americans and aerospace leaders.

Human Connection. People read mission statements. People implement the mission. Consequently, an effective mission statement includes a human connection that suggests how real people connect with the organization. For example, the Honor Guard mission quoted above implies that its members are called to represent the best traditions of the Air Force. You know what you're getting yourself into by joining the Honor Guard, just by reading the mission. Likewise, the human side of a mission statement provides a starting point for individuals to see how their personal goals mesh with organizational goals. If your dream is to see the world and be part of an elite team, the Honor Guard mission suggests that your goals are closely aligned with theirs.[33] In other words, an effective mission statement not only tells what the organization does, but also alludes to basic human needs including economic or paycheck needs, social needs, the need for personal growth, spiritual fulfillment and personal satisfaction.[34]

Logical Sequencing. Mission statements exemplify a natural logic. They bring order to chaos. Their specificity defines the organization and its activities. Why is this helpful? The natural way to accomplish something meaningful is (1) to specify a purpose, (2) identify the issues or challenges standing in your way, and (3) debate the ideas to find a workable solution.* A mission statement accomplishes steps 1 and 2 for you.[35] Going back to Northrop Grumman's mission, for example, step 1 tells us their purpose is to "provide systems and technologies" (a high-minded way of saying "build weapons for the military). Step 2 tells us that some of the challenges include building weapons that are not only useful to our troops, but our allies as well, and that our troops need to fight in every possible battlespace – "from undersea to outer space...." Read the Northrop Grumman mission statement and you're ready to get to work on step 3, finding solutions.

Senior CAP leaders

Teachers / AEMs

Cadets

ES customers

Elected officials

Senior members

Air Force leaders

Pilots

And more cadets...

*Fine Print: We are speaking generally about the process of accomplishing goals. Do not read this as the definitive problem-solving process.

People Write Mission Statements

Who implements the mission? People! Therefore people from every facet of the organization should have a say in developing the mission statement. Ignore people, and your mission statement becomes mere words that no one cares about.

Measurable Achievement. How do you know if your organization is successful? A straightforward question calls for a straightforward answer. Successful teams accomplish the mission. Therefore, an effective mission statement is measurable.[36] Again, consider the Honor Guard. Is the Honor Guard consistently on-the-go, traveling and hosting performances? If not, they aren't "representing Airmen. . . to the world." Are their performances of world-class caliber? If not, they aren't "protecting the standards [and] perfecting the image." An effective mission statement offers the organization a yardstick for measuring its success.

The "How To" Process for Developing a Mission Statement

Knowing what a mission statement is supposed to do and how it does that work, the next question is, "How do you develop one?"

Involve the Troops. The first principle to keep in mind is that good leaders involve their people in developing the mission statement. Tap their minds for good ideas. In turn, they'll commit to it. The alternative – a mission statement developed by the top leaders and pushed downhill – is likely to amount to nothing more than mere words on a page. "Many organizations have a mission statement," observes one expert, "but typically people aren't committed to it because they aren't involved in developing it; consequently it's not part of the culture, [which] by definition, assumes shared vision and values."[37]

Consider the Stakeholders' Perspectives. To be successful, an organization has to satisfy its key stakeholders. Keep the customer happy. Therefore, when developing a mission statement, it is important to analyze the mission from the stakeholders' perspective.[38] To do this, first determine who the stakeholders are. Be wide-ranging in your thinking. The diagram at right hints that you may have a lot more stakeholders than you think. Second, figure out how each stakeholder measures your organization's success. Make an educated guess, or, in the case of your top two or three stakeholders, you might ask them directly. Through this process of stakeholder analysis, you force your organization to take a dispassionate view toward its mission. As a result, you are more apt to define your mission in a way that leads toward happy customers and organizational success.

Who has a stake in the Cadet Program? This diagram identifies some of the major and peripheral stakeholders in the CAP Cadet Program, in no particular order.

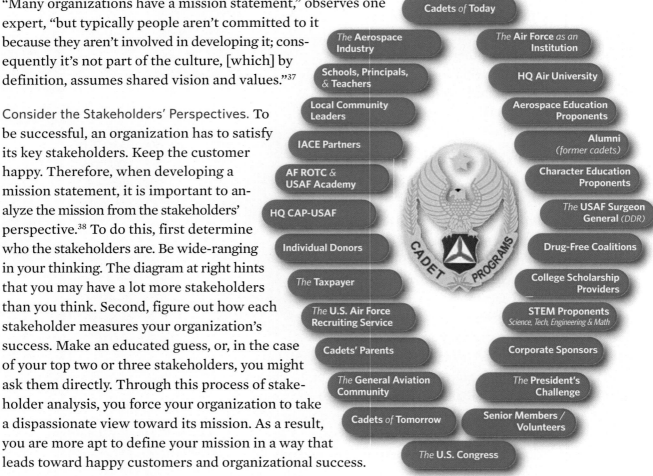

Cadets *of* Today

The Aerospace Industry

The **Air Force** *as an* Institution

Schools, Principals, & Teachers

HQ Air University

Local Community Leaders

Aerospace Education Proponents

IACE Partners

Alumni *(former cadets)*

AF ROTC & USAF Academy

Character Education Proponents

HQ CAP-USAF

The USAF Surgeon General *(DDR)*

Individual Donors

Drug-Free Coalitions

The Taxpayer

College Scholarship Providers

The U.S. Air Force Recruiting Service

STEM Proponents *Science, Tech, Engineering & Math*

Cadets' Parents

Corporate Sponsors

The General Aviation Community

The President's Challenge

Cadets *of* Tomorrow

Senior Members / Volunteers

The U.S. Congress

Fine Print: Notice that stakeholders can be a wide-ranging institution, represented here by "The Air Force," while also including subunits of that institution, represented here by "CAP-USAF," "Air Force Recruiting Service," and "AFROTC," etc. Think in terms of the future, too. The Cadet Program serves today's cadets, but its leaders have to ensure it will be ready for little brothers and sisters when they come of age.

Reflect Upon Questions That Get to Your Inner Core. Various experts advocate different procedures for developing the mission statement. But one thing is clear: the organization has to ask itself some tough questions and do some soul-searching.

1. Who are we? What does that imply? For example, we are cadets, and that implies patriotic young people who are proud to wear the uniform. Moreover, cadets are young leaders, but they are not children, so that fact helps locate the Cadet Program within a certain segment of society.

2. What are the basic needs we exist to meet? Again, stay high-minded and resist the urge to reply with a trite, "Make a profit." A cadet organization exists to help young people develop leadership skills, test-fly potential careers, have fun, stay away from drugs, and the like.

3. What do we do to meet those needs? In the Cadet Program, we teach leadership, go flying, do physical training, hold summer encampments, permit cadets to rub elbows with Air Force personnel, etc. Notice that the items here – going flying or holding encampments for example – do not represent the cadets' basic needs. Rather, these items are merely the means to achieve broader, more high-minded needs.

4. What are our values? This is an easy one for a cadet organization. We simply point to our Core Values. But recognize that different organizations espouse different values. We're all against lying and cheating. But to describe Apple's values, for example, words like creativity and innovation come to mind. Consider the IRS, and words like accuracy, fairness, and respect for the law are more appropriate. Why are values important in developing the mission? They drive the mission and help define the organization. Informed by its values, Apple's mission will speak to being a high-tech company. The IRS's mission will speak to its duty to enforce tax laws fairly and perform a public service.

5. What makes us unique? A mission statement ought to help one organization differentiate itself from similar organizations. Both the Army and the Air Force, for example, exist to defend the United States. Both do that by developing warfighters. Both espouse similar values of patriotism, honor, and valor. But, of course, the Air Force is unique in that it fights in air, space, and cyberspace, while the Army is primarily a ground force. This is an obvious example; what separates your organization from its competitors may be more subtle.

All told, crafting an effective mission statement requires leaders to do three things. (1) Involve the troops in the process, (2) think about the organization from the stakeholders' or customers' perspective, and (3) ask a series of tough, soul-searching questions.

Culture & The Mission

The IRS & Apple are two totally different organizations, each trying to succeed in its own way.

Think of the IRS and what values might come to mind?
• Accuracy
• Fairness
• Respect for Law

Think of Apple and what values might come to mind?
• Creativity
• Innovation
• The Cool Factor

The lesson is this: Whatever an organization values will affect how it understands itself and its mission.

THE COMMANDER & HUMAN CAPITAL

Surround yourself with good people. Countless great leaders have echoed that proverb. Indeed, one of the key responsibilities of command is the task of recruiting a great team.[39] Human capital management is a term that insists that people are assets. The word "capital" is borrowed from economics, where it basically means "money in the bank." Therefore, the term "human capital" conveys a belief that good people are like gold. You want to find the most valuable people you can, and you want to hold on to them as you would a chest full of gold.

A person's knowledge, skills, values, and intangible personal qualities count as valuable assets. Likewise, the time, money, and energy an organization puts toward educating people and providing them with fair compensation and health care are not a drag on the organization but an investment. These are some of the principles suggested by the term "human capital."[40]

What are some of the issues commanders face in regard to human capital? We'll look at job descriptions, job interviews, hiring decisions, and firing decisions.

Human Capital
The term "human capital" conveys the idea that having good people on your team is even better than having money in the bank.

JOB DESCRIPTIONS

OBJECTIVES:
9. List the questions that a good job description must answer.
10. Describe basic principles to follow when writing a job description.

"A job description is simply a clear, concise depiction of a job's duties and requirements."[41] It is the authoritative, indispensible definition of what a particular job is all about. A good job description will answer three basic questions:[42]

(1) Why does this job exist? What is the basic purpose?
(2) What does the job accomplish?
(3) How does this job relate to other jobs in the organization?

When developing a job description, keep the following principles in mind:

Joint Authorship. An authoritarian leader will merely present the subordinate with the job description and tell that person to get to work. In contrast, servant leaders take a more enlightened approach by recognizing the need for job descriptions to be documents of "joint authorship," at least after the subordinate acquires some experience and gets to know the job. After all, who really understands what needs to be done better than the person in the job? Using joint authorship to develop a job description helps ensure that boss and subordinate both agree on what the job entails.[43]

Fine Print: In chapter 8, you learned how to write a résumé and prepare for a job interview. Now we'll consider the hiring process from the leader's perspective. At this stage in your life, you won't be doing much hiring, apart from selecting a staff in your home squadron or perhaps at encampment. Therefore, try to use this glimpse into the hiring process from the manager's perspective to round out your own job-seeking and interviewing skills. If you can appreciate the challenges that hiring managers face, you can be that much more successful when you interview for summer jobs, colleges, etc.

Job Functions. A job description lists the main functions of the position. It outlines the key responsibilities and offers a good sense of what the job is all about. For example, the job functions performed by a cadet flight sergeant include things like leading the flight in drill, instructing cadets on basic leadership topics, monitoring cadets' uniforms and enforcing standards, etc. Generally speaking, everything that the person does in the job should be traceable back to one of the functions outlined on the job description.

Performance Standards. We know the basic tasks entailed in the job, but we need more information. What are the standards of performance? Productivity quotas, acceptable rates of error, deadlines for completing projects, and the like define the job's minimum level of acceptable performance.[44] Managers would want a supermarket cashier to give back the exact change for every transaction, but mistakes happen. Perhaps a fair standard is for the cashier's drawer to be over or under a maximum of $1 at the end of the day. More abstract jobs like cadet commander of an encampment are harder to measure. Perhaps deadlines are the best performance standards. Deliver to the commandant a staff plan by March, a training plan by April, and a cadet handbook by May for the July encampment. Each job is different, but the principle is clear: a job description must list basic standards of performance so that the boss and the team member both know what counts as a job well done. And, going back to the idea of servant leadership, these standards can be jointly-authored. The servant leader's role is to ensure that high-speed team members do not set unrealistically high goals for themselves, and that timid folks learn that they will be expected to produce a bit more than they would if they set their own pace.[45]

In the final assessment, a job description is a valuable leadership tool. It is a starting point for the boss and subordinate alike to agree upon what needs to be done and how well it must be done. Circumstances change as the team grows and pursues new goals, so leaders should revisit job descriptions periodically.[46]

INTERVIEW SKILLS FOR THE HIRING MANAGER

OBJECTIVES:

11. Identify challenges that an interviewer must overcome during a job interviewer.
12. Recall practical tips for conducting an interview.

The personal interview is the most important event in the hiring process. Leaders can read a résumé to form a general impression, but for a more thorough understanding of what a candidate has to offer, the interview is indispensable. Why? Interviews allow leaders to see candidates' people skills in action. Attitude is on display. The

Job Functions
A job description lists the main functions and key responsibilities for that position. A flight sergeant's job description will probably include functions like these:

Drill the Flight

Teach & Mentor

Motivate & Assist

Lead in Ceremonies

give and take of discussion is a venue for gauging communication skills. Moreover, leaders can watch candidates think on their feet as the candidates consider and respond to the interviewer's questions. Whether candidates report on time or arrive late speaks to their professionalism, as does their dress and appearance. In short, the interview is the only place in the hiring process where a candidate's intangible qualities are on display.

Key Challenges for the Interviewer. Enduring a job interview is not an everyday experience. People are naturally nervous. It's normal for candidates to feel a little weird, and that awkwardness is bound to come through. What are some of the key challenges that interviewers encounter in the high-stakes environment of the job interview?

Candidates wear masks to interviews, and most people exaggerate their abilities.[47] General nervousness added to the pressure to present oneself in the best possible light equals inauthenticity. This is not to say candidates are inherently dishonest. But a key challenge for interviewers is to get behind the superficial personae.

A second challenge is to encourage the interview to be a two-way dialogue. It is in everyone's interest for the candidate to discern if the hiring organization is a good fit for his or her personal goals, as much as it is in the boss's interest to ensure the candidate is a good match for the job.[48] The boss interviews the candidate. The candidate interviews the organization.

Make a new friend and certain questions naturally come up. How old are you? Are you in a relationship? Do you go to church? What's your political affiliation? Each of those questions is inappropriate and illegal to ask during a job interview. Americans' belief in equal opportunity puts questions of that sort off limits. Therefore, a third challenge is to stick to questions that directly relate to the job.[49]

The Interview is a Structured Process. From your studies in chapter 8, you know that job applicants must prepare for interviews. Likewise, interviewers must prepare by carefully designing the interview so that they can make well-informed hiring decisions. A boss who simply tries to "wing it" is apt to experience meaningless conversation, not an intelligent dialogue.[50] A good interview is structured around a series of thoughtful questions, with each question having some connection to the job description. This is not to say that an interviewer can't be spontaneous. However, every applicant deserves the opportunity to respond to the same questions.[51] And for the sake of holding every applicant to the same standard, interviewers should rate the candidates against the same scorecard.[52]

A Standard Scorecard for a Structured Process
Keep score during interviews. Scorecards help you evaluate each applicant against the same standard.

Job Search Scorecard

	Curry	Arnold	Feik	Wright
Relevant Experience 7 pts max	4	4	6	2
Training & Education 5 pt max	3	2	4	1
Interview Responses 5 pts max	2	2	4	1
Communication Skills 3 pts max	1	3	2	1
Other 3 pts max	2 Eager!	0	2 Smart!	0
Totals	12	11	18	5

PRACTICAL TIPS FOR INTERVIEWERS

What are some trade secrets of successful interviewers? Here are some practical tips that have proven successful.[53, 54]

- Read the candidate's résumé before the interview. Highlight significant strengths and items you want to know more about.

- Warmly greet the candidate. Shake hands. Offer a bottle of water. Begin with easy chit-chat. Place the candidate at ease. It's in everyone's interest for the candidate to feel comfortable.

- Compliment the candidate by recognizing that he is obviously a good candidate by virtue of being invited to interview. Explain that the purpose of the interview is to see if he is a good match for what the organization needs at this moment, and whether the team is a good fit for the candidate's personal goals and needs.

- Really listen to the candidate. Practice chapter 2's active listening skills.

- Get beyond the canned, rehearsed answer. Use rolling "Why?" questions to probe deeper into the topic.

- Ask open-ended questions. "Why are you attracted to this job opening?" "Tell me about a time that you overcame a tough situation."

- Ask some situational questions. "If selected as our first sergeant, how would you handle a cadet whose hair was out of regulation for three weeks?"

- Take notes during the conversation, but not so many that you are unable to really listen. If interviewing more than a handful of candidates, it can be easy to forget who said what, and what each candidate has to offer.

- Just before concluding, give the candidate a final opportunity to make final remarks. Ask, "Is there anything else you want us to know about your qualifications?" and "Do you have any final questions?"

- Shake hands and thank the candidate for her time.

- Immediately evaluate the candidate based on the criteria you listed on your scorecard.

MAKING A HIRING DECISION

OBJECTIVES:

13. List and briefly define four hazards a hiring manager must overcome with new hires.
14. Appreciate the principles of dismissing staff with dignity.

Hiring Authority. Who should make the hiring decision? Most experts believe that the person who will supervise the new hire ought to be empowered to decide which candidate is best. Acknowledging that a higher-level boss also has a stake in the decision, some experts suggest that the higher boss have veto authority over a subordinate leader's decision.[55]

Hazards in Decision-Making. The hiring manager's challenge is to find the best possible candidate at the current moment. Before deciding who that person is, hiring managers need to be wary of some potential hazards.

Halo Effect. People have a tendency to favor people who come from a background similar to their own or share the same interests.[56] This is known as the halo effect because the person appears to be a "perfect angel" for no good reason. Hiring managers ought to demand specificity from themselves. It's not enough to say, "I am impressed by Candidate X." The manager should identify the candidate's precise qualities and connect those attributes to the job's needs.

Wow, you like playing Call of Duty? Me, too. You're hired! You're my new exec!

The Halo Effect
Not going to happen! The absurdity of this example only underscores the point that the halo effect has no place in the hiring process. You just know that a 4-star is going to make hiring decisions based on job requirements, not shared hobbies. Clear-minded leaders select the candidate who is best prepared to fill the job's needs.

Attraction Bias. The cadet captain presents himself better than the other candidates in terms of appearance, but who knows, maybe that zombie is the best person for the job. Don't fault the undead for their ugliness, awful smell and unsightly wounds – that would be an example of attraction bias.

Attraction Bias. The best candidate is not necessarily a potential movie star. According to a well-respected study, "The bias in favor of physically attractive people is robust, with attractive people being perceived as more sociable, happier, and more successful than unattractive people."[57] Another study found that obese individuals earn less than similarly qualified peers.[58] Hiring managers need to be mindful of the attraction bias, and remember that good looks have nothing to do with the ability to perform the job well.

Impressive References. If a candidate showed you a letter of reference from a U.S. senator, would you be impressed? In reviewing letters of recommendation, look for insights into the candidate's experiences and personal qualities that are relevant to the job. The rank of the person giving the reference is not always relevant. Sometimes it merely indicates the candidate has friends in high places.

Nepotism.[59] Hiring managers aren't supposed to play favorites. Nepotism is the practice of favoring relatives or friends in professional matters, especially in hiring. President John F. Kennedy was harshly criticized for naming his younger brother Robert F. Kennedy as U.S. attorney general. Congress enacted anti-nepotism laws as a result. The general rule is that family members should not be in the same chain of command. Big companies and government agencies have strict anti-nepotism rules. On the other hand, family-owned small businesses cannot avoid nepotism, simply by virtue of their being family-run. Likewise, a volunteer organization that encourages family participation, such as CAP, is apt to experience messy personnel situations that would never arise in the military, with its anti-nepotism policies.

The Family Business
Nepotism is the practice of favoring relatives or friends in hiring decisions. President Kennedy (right) picked his brother Bobby (left) to be attorney general. Another brother, Teddy (center), served in JFK's old Senate seat.[60] Leaders can be criticized for nepotism because merit, not personal connections, is supposed to guide hiring decisions.

A FAMILY TRADITION *of* PUBLIC SERVICE

The Old Man of the Mountain was a series of five granite cliff ledges that, when viewed from a particular angle, resembled a great stone face.

For 12,000 years this natural rock formation overlooked New Hampshire's Franconia Notch, but by 1905 it was apparent that he could collapse.

Turnbuckles, epoxy, and a special membrane of wire and cloth held the Old Man's massive features together. Each year, the official caretaker, Niels F.F. Nielsen Jr., and a team of volunteers, would give the Old Man a "shave and a haircut."

After 39 years of service, Nielsen could no longer perform the rough, physical work. By order of the governor, the position of Official Caretaker was transferred to Nielsen's son David.[61]

But wait. Don't most organizations, especially governments that are accountable to the people, have rules against nepotism? One might expect the state would advertise the position opening and interview multiple candidates before selecting a new caretaker. Instead, the governor and state legislature were content to allow the father to pass the torch to the son. Rather than cry, "Nepotism!," state officials were grateful that a second generation of Nielsens were willing to serve.

In volunteer settings like CAP and the caring for the Old Man, whole families get involved. On a basic human level that's a wonderful thing. From a leadership perspective, the challenge is to encourage and appreciate a family's noble service without singling them out for special treatment.

For example, everyone in CAP surely knows of a cadet whose mom or dad holds a leadership position. The Cadet Program could not continue if parents and their kids and those cadets' siblings were barred from

membership. Volunteer organizations cannot enforce the same strict rules regarding family members and the chain of command that are standard practice in big companies.

Maintaining the team's harmony is difficult when some of the team members' relationships run deeper than others. It's a delicate balancing act, and further evidence that leadership in a volunteer setting is more challenging than leadership in a business or military setting, by virtue of the complex people matters and potential favoritism.

Returning to the story of the Old Man's upkeep, from a practical standpoint, only the family and a handful of other volunteers knew what the Old Man required, could identify the individual ledges that formed the profile, understood the tried-and-true methods for keeping him together, or had the experience to perform work while suspended 1,400 feet above Profile Lake. This

was a family tradition of public service, not a scandal of one family's misuse of power. The state legislature was right to perpetuate the Nielsens' vocation.

Fittingly, when Niels F.F. Nielsen Jr. passed away, son David placed his ashes in the Old Man's left eye socket.

The Nielsen family's careful stewardship preserved the Old Man for 43 years, until the Old Man finally succumbed to the elements in 2003. The family's service enabled millions of people to enjoy the company of the Old Man, New Hampshire's most beloved citizen.

In short, the hiring manager needs to consciously remember that she is not choosing a lunch partner or trying to make a new friend. Rather, the manager is responsible for selecting the best possible candidate on behalf of the organization.

Trade-Offs. One human capital expert advises, "Do not attempt to find the perfect candidate . . . Rarely, if ever, does that person exist."[62] Therefore, hiring is a matter of making trade-offs, of weighing the pros and cons. The diagram at right presents a mix of imperfect candidates to illustrate the point. When using a standardized scorecard to rank candidates, the math makes the decision for the manager. And yet the intangible qualities of each individual somehow have a place, too. Hiring decisions are tough, and vital. A CEO of a major company observed, "Nothing we do is more important than hiring. . . At the end of the day, you bet on people, not strategies."[63]

DISMISSING WITH DIGNITY

Our final topic on the subject of human capital is dismissal. Letting someone go is an unpleasant event for boss and subordinate alike. A real person is profoundly affected, and so is that individual's family. In the adult workplace, a human resources professional should be consulted before terminating an employee. For our purposes here, the goal is simply for you as a cadet officer to appreciate two principles:

- The boss should treat the subordinate with perfect dignity.
- You can bounce back after being fired and find professional success elsewhere.

A Last Resort. Because dismissing someone has such an effect on their livelihood, termination should be a last resort. Experts frequently use the metaphor of "strike three." That is, leaders owe subordinates ample coaching, fair warning, added training, formal counseling, and the like before they are fired. The general mood ought to be that all alternatives have been tried. Except in the case of a single, egregious act (e.g.: workplace violence, theft), terminations should not come as a surprise. The sense of failure is mutual because, as one expert put it, "both parties share some responsibility for having chosen each other, and for making the relationship grow and succeed afterward."[64]

Respect for the Individual. In the very least, the subordinate deserves to be terminated in private. Calmly and clearly tell the individual that you are letting them go and briefly state the reason, which should be no surprise. All money owed the employee should be delivered on the spot. Even more, because most bosses expect employees to pay them the courtesy of giving two weeks' notice before quitting, a terminated employee should receive at least two weeks' pay as severance.[65] Suffice it to say that the tone throughout this unpleasant process must be one of politeness and empathy. Make no mistake: Donald Trump's famous catchphrase from *The Apprentice,* "You're fired!" represents terrible leadership, atrocious manners, and a mean spirit.

Leadership Lessons from a Bad Example
Donald Trump's famous catchphrase from *The Apprentice* does not show respect for the individual who is being dismissed, nor does it acknowledge that boss and subordinate alike share some responsibility for making their relationship work.

LEADERSHIP TOOLS FOR THE COMMANDER

In chapters 1-10, you were presented with a number of tools for leadership development. At this stage in your cadet career, it's time to tie all those concepts together using a single model: the Full Range Leadership Model. As your level of authority increases, so should your use of delegation. Effective delegation for commanders is another skill covered in this section.

An Air Force Perspective
The Air Force's Squadron Officer College advocates FRLM as the best tool for development of successful leadership behaviors.

FULL RANGE LEADERSHIP

OBJECTIVES:

15. Define the terms "laissez-faire," "management by exception," and "contingent reward" as used in the Full Range Leadership Model.
16. Describe each of the 4I's of transformational leadership in the Full Range Leadership Model.

So many principles inform our understanding of how we should lead. It would be helpful to bring those teachings together under a single framework so that we have an integrated model of leadership in all its stripes. Recognizing this need, scholars Bernard Bass and Bruce Avolio synthesized what they knew about leadership, based on scientific evidence, and produced a full range leadership model (FRLM).[66] This is a full spectrum of leadership, from its colorless vacuity to shining fulfillment. In visualizing the relationships between multiple leadership approaches, FRLM describes how leadership behaviors interact and can be used effectively across their full range.

Before examining FRLM, we should revisit a quote from chapter 3. "Bad leadership implies no leadership," according to James MacGregor Burns, the intellectual godfather to Bass and Avolio. "I contend that there is nothing neutral about leadership; it is valued as a moral necessity."[67] FRLM accepts that premise. Moreover, it views authentic leadership as the flourishing of moral values. Real leaders lead by example. They embody the high-minded qualities they espouse. In this way, FRLM builds upon Aristotle's idea of the *telos* of happiness (think back to the earlier section on virtue ethics in chapter 9). As an aspiring young leader, you have some capacity to lead. Your leadership flourishes when you perfect that capacity by repeatedly choosing positive approaches to leadership. That striving for excellence leads to virtue. FRLM teaches that because you have the capacity to mentor, challenge, inspire, and model, you must lead in a way that brings forth those capacities. To do otherwise would be to waste your potential and embrace an impoverished sense of leadership.

Fine Print: Not all leaders are commanders, but all commanders must be leaders. This section on FRLM might fit nearly anywhere in *Learn to Lead*. In fact, back in chapter 7 you studied each component of FRLM without realizing it. We're including FRLM in this chapter on command because one theme we've been emphasizing is that the commander brings together disparate parts to form a team. In a similar way, FRLM shows that different expressions of leadership come together to provide us a complete view of the whole of leadership.

AVOID	DIRECT			INFLUENCE			
ABSENT	**TRANSACTIONAL**			**TRANSFORMATIONAL**			
Laissez-Faire	Management by Exception		Contingent Reward	Individual Consideration	Intellectual Stimulation	Inspirational Motivation	Idealized Influence
	Passive	Active					
LF	MBE-P	MBE-A	CR	IC	IS	IM	II
"Delay"	"Fix"	"Control"	"Reward"	"Mentor"	"Challenge"	"Inspire"	"Model"
PASSIVE	CORRECTIVE	TRANSACTIONAL		TRANSFORMATIONAL			

A full range leadership model, as depicted by the Air Force version of Bass's and Avolio's standard diagram.

ANALYSIS OF THE FULL RANGE LEADERSHIP MODEL

Examine the diagram above. FRLM is an adaptive approach to leadership that considers the leader, the follower, and the mission. The graphic shows a cafeteria line of leadership behaviors. On the left side, laissez-faire behavior represents an absence of true leadership. The center focuses on the effective but potentially manipulative brand of leadership called transactional. The far right side showcases a flourishing of leadership in transformational leadership. The goal is for every leader to develop skills that allow him to utilize transactional or transformational leadership to the highest effect. Put another way, FRLM is **not** a situational approach; the message is not to use laissez-faire in some situations or management by exception in others. Rather, FRLM presents multiple approaches across a spectrum. Those approaches becomes progressively more effective, yet more demanding of leadership skill.[68]

Is FRLM really a full explanation of leadership? Maybe yes, maybe no. Bass and Avolio chose the term "full range" to nudge other scholars. If FRLM is not full range, what's missing?[70]

ABSENCE OF LEADERSHIP

Laissez-faire (LF) is the absence of leadership. LF is a boss who plays hooky from work. It's the non-leader whose behavior shows no signs of being concerned about the mission, nor her people.[69] No wonder our model regards LF as the most impoverished view of leadership.

TRANSACTIONAL LEADERSHIP

MBE is management by exception. MBE is a form of transactional leadership. You do something, and I react. Or I do something, and you react.

In one type of MBE called "passive" MBE or MBE-P, the leader waits for mistakes to happen, steps in to fix them, and then steps back again into an almost laissez-faire stance until some other problem

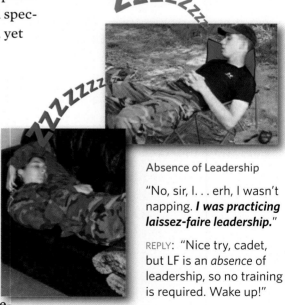

ZZZZZZ

Absence of Leadership

"No, sir, I . . . erh, I wasn't napping. *I was practicing laissez-faire leadership.*"

REPLY: "Nice try, cadet, but LF is an *absence* of leadership, so no training is required. Wake up!"

develops.[71] This "leader" is like a robot that comes alive only when something goes wrong. Work for the MBE-P boss, and the only time you see him is when a team member goofs up. Your dealings with the boss are often accompanied by negative feelings, and you're definitely not inspired to up your game.

A second type of MBE is called "active" MBE or MBE-A. Here, the boss is not a slumbering robot like above, but is highly visible to the team and can often be found checking up on everyone's work, looking for errors.[72] MBE-A is more effective than MBE-P because at least the boss is actively engaged in the team's efforts. The problem, though, is that the focus remains on the negative. The boss is more akin to a critic who is constantly on patrol than a leader who brings the team to higher levels.

Contingent Reward (CR) is a form of transactional leadership that focuses on getting things done. Here, the leader uses incentives to encourage people to do the right things. The leader sets goals for the team, but the leader/team relationship might be perceived as cold, impersonal, and seemingly defined by a contract (if not a real contract, an implied one).[73] Meet the leader's goals, earn a cookie. Fail to meet the goals, no cookie. CR creates a predictable, consistent environment, and that sense of security fulfills an important need. Again, CR is basically positive; note that the emphasis is on rewarding performance, not in punishing non-performance. Experts have found that CR is "generally effective in building base levels of trust and commitment in followers."[74] Fair enough, but don't you think good leadership involves a bit more?

Transactional Leadership: Final Analysis. Management by exception and contingent reward are valid tools available to the leader, especially when operating at the tactical and operational levels of leadership. However, FRLM insists that a transformational approach to leadership is superior. Scientific data bears that out. Moreover, displaying too much MBE and CR is not leading but working tit-for-tat, trying to pass off manipulation as a form of leadership.[75] The team will work just hard enough to get by. Only through transformational leadership can a leader truly bring the team to new accomplishments.

Management by Exception - Passive MBE-P
In the MBE-P variant of leadership, the boss is like a robot that comes alive only when something goes wrong.

Contingent Reward
Leaders use incentives to encourage followers to perform in the CR approach. Meet the goals, get a cookie. Experts say that CR is generally effective in building a basic level of trust between leader and follower.

TRANSFORMATIONAL LEADERSHIP

Now comes transformational leadership. From chapter 7 you know that transformational leadership is where the leader "strives to heighten the motivation and morality of himself and his followers."[76] And of course, to "transform" something implies that you are changing it into something better. The leader is the midwife for new cultures and value systems. Within transformational leadership we have four components, the 4I's described below.

Individual Consideration (IC) is where the leader develops people. He or she listens to, coaches, and teaches the individual members. Put another way, IC means to mentor someone on a one-on-one basis. Instead of viewing team members as easily replaceable cogs in the machine, a leader who shows strong IC has empathy and sees each individual as a unique person.[77] Research shows that people respect a leader who treats them as individuals, and those good feelings translate into increased mission effectiveness.

Intellectual Stimulation (IS) requires the leader to challenge team members to really think. Instead of the leader viewing himself or herself as the all-knowing source of all wisdom, he turns to the team members and engages their brainpower. The team wins because now there's not just the leader's

PROFILES OF TRANSFORMATIONAL LEADERS

More Than Cheerleaders		JOHN GLENN	ROSA PARKS	JOAN OF ARC	ABRAHAM LINCOLN
Transformational leadership has a lot to do with changing people's values for the better, but as the highest form of leadership, it goes well beyond mere cheerleading.	**IC**	Set the pace and developed his fellow Mercury astronauts into a cohesive team	Organized and developed the early leaders of the Montgomery Improvement Association	A mere peasant and young girl, Joan had to convince many individuals in power to take her seriously	Developed and held together a cabinet, army, and navy to save the Union
	IS	A champion of math and science to generations of young Americans	Nonviolence showed that the answer to democracy's challenges lay in reasoned discourse	Quick-witted during a politically motivated trial, the uneducated teen stupefied her interrogators	One of the most learned and thought-provoking communicators of all time
IC: Develop other people IS: Promote the use of brainpower IM: Inspire confidence about the future II: Lead by personal example	**IM**	Supreme confidence in the face of danger showed that space exploration was worth the risks	Refusal to move to the back of the bus launched a nation-wide civil rights movement	Lead common soldiers and peasants in combat against a larger, better trained, and better equipped English force	How many millions recall words from his Gettysburg Address or Second Inaugural?
	II	A squeaky-clean character combined with brains and bravery – who wouldn't want to be like Glenn?	One of the few private citizens to lay in honor under the Capitol Rotunda upon death, thereby distinguishing her as a truly idealized American leader	Her purity, faith, and patriotism made her the national heroine of France and a saint	"In this temple, as in the hearts of the people for whom he saved the Union, the memory of Abraham Lincoln is enshrined forever"

IDEALIZED INFLUENCE on 9/11

Through idealized influence, the leader exemplifies, through consistent behaviors, what each individual should become. Here's David Letterman, shortly after 9/11, paying tribute to the idealized influence of Mayor Rudolph Giuliani's leadership.

"If you're like me, and you're watching and you're confused and depressed and irritated and angry and full of grief, and you don't know how to behave and you're not sure what to do and you don't really... because we've never been through this before... all you had to do at any moment was watch the Mayor. Watch how this guy behaved. Watch how this guy conducted himself. Watch what this guy did. Listen to what this guy said. Rudolph Giuliani is the personification of courage."[78]

– DAVID LETTERMAN

intellect working on the problem, but everyone is contributing new thoughts and different perspectives.[79] Individuals win, too, because their work now engages their whole person, so they can really flourish in that Aristotelian sense mentioned earlier. Work means learning, and learning brings success, confidence, and personal satisfaction.

Inspirational Motivation (IM) calls on the leader to express confidence in the team and encourage its members to become better than they think they can be.[80] Put another way, an IM leader is a visionary who is not only able to articulate "headlines of tomorrow," but also to make the team believe those awesome accomplishments are within their reach. But do not be confused. A cheerleader is not an IM leader. Cheering and encouragement are great, but IM is about motivating people to accomplish a *well-articulated* vision.

Idealized Influence (II) is another way to say "leadership by example." The II leader is a role model. He or she exemplifies, through consistent, everyday behaviors, what each individual team member should become.[81] Moreover, the followers know that the leader is having a deep effect upon them, and they attribute exhibited behaviors and attitudes to their leader/role model. If you want to learn the team's core values, simply watch the II leader because they'll be on display. This is the most excellent sense of leadership because the leader's espoused beliefs and actions are one and the same. The leader is a leader because she leads well. You can't be an authentic transformational leader if you only talk the talk; you have to walk the walk.

In the final analysis, FRLM presents a complete view of leadership. On the far left of the diagram, we see a pathetic excuse for leadership; then we see increasingly more active and positive expressions of leadership; until on the extreme right, the individual actually becomes, through personal actions, the very best example of what the team is aspiring to.

PRACTICAL APPLICATION: CADET OFFICERS & FRLM

Transactional leadership is about the mission and the present. At the individual level this is where the rubber meets the road for front-line leaders. Transactional leadership is not only effective and appropriate in many situations, it is often vital to employee satisfaction and mission accomplishment. Many people need a bonus, a ribbon, or a simple compliment to feel appreciated. Think of the civilian company that uses a bonus system to reward performance (CR) or how an in-ranks inspection (MBE) is used to validate standards. Those things cannot be replaced by transformational leadership alone.

Transformational leadership is about people and the future. At the individual level, this is the strategic development of leaders and followers, followers who will become the future leaders. The challenge is at the operational level, where balancing both transactional and transformational leadership is most often seen. Cadet officers, much like Air Force company grade officers, work primarily at the operational level. They are no longer front-line supervisors, but middle-managers at the squadron level.

TACTICAL LEVEL
Transactional behavior is common

Consider the following guidelines when applying FRLM:

- At the tactical level, leaders typically employ transactional behaviors.

- At the operational level, leaders balance transactional and transformational behaviors.

- At the strategic level, leaders rely heavily on transformational behaviors.

OPERATIONAL LEVEL
Transactional & transformational behaviors are often in balance

Taken to its extreme, any FRLM behavior can be bad if used inappropriately or exclusively. MBE can become micromanagement, IM can become cheerleading, CR can become punishment, and on and on. Too much emphasis on transformational leadership can consume valuable time, especially at the operational and tactical levels.

In practice, the message of FRLM is simple: don't sleepwalk through your time as a commander, or in any capacity as a leader. Constantly evaluate your leadership behaviors in respect to the FRLM spectrum. If you find you are behaving as a laissez-faire or transactional leader most of the time, ask yourself how you might develop new behaviors to embody the 4I's of transformational leadership. Better still, map your 360-degree feedback (discussed later in this chapter) to FRLM to see what kind of leader others see you as. Further, go people-watching. Observe other leaders in action. Try to discern where their behaviors fall upon the FRLM spectrum.[82] In short, FRLM is a great tool for comprehending leadership in its different gradations.

STRATEGIC LEVEL
Transformational behavior is heavily relied upon

DELEGATION SKILLS FOR A HECTIC WORLD [83]

OBJECTIVES:

17. Describe what is meant by the leadership skill of delegation.
18. Define the term "vital shift."
19. Name some benefits of practicing effective delegation.
20. List and briefly define the three key words in effective delegation.
21. Recall the four steps to follow for effective delegation.
22. Name some common mistakes in delegation.

In the quote above, Roosevelt was in essence describing the art of delegation — a critical leadership skill indeed. As a supervisor, you'll have the managerial latitude of delegating authority to your people whenever you determine it necessary and in the best interests of your organization's mission. Using this privilege carefully can reap not only substantial benefits for your operation, but can generate meaningful advantages to you, your people, and the Air Force.

Delegation usually isn't as simple as just telling people to do work or giving orders. We have to learn how to delegate the work in such a way that people will accept it, appreciate the role they're in, and keep coming back for more. Delegation as a skill or process takes practice. In most instances, the delegation process involves more than simply saying "Joe, from now on you're in charge of keeping the car filled with gas." This chapter will give you an opportunity to learn about this skill — delegation.

This entire section is reprinted nearly verbatim from AFJROTC, *Leadership Education IV, Principles of Management,* (Maxwell AFB: Air University, 1999), 112-123. Many thanks to our HQ AFJROTC friends for their continued partnership with CAP Cadet Programs.

WHAT IS DELEGATION?

Delegation is a leadership skill which involves the development of an understanding between a leader and a follower about how they'll share authority and responsibility for accomplishing their portion of the mission.

It seems obvious that even the worst supervisor should appreciate the importance of effective delegation practices and should be skilled at using them. Right? Wrong! Delegation is hard work and is a slippery skill to master. Delegation calls for planning ahead, coordinating activities, establishing goals, clearly drawing lines of authority and responsibility, and having the courage to give tasks to subordinates and trust in their ability to carry them out.

Many a well-meaning supervisor delegates improperly or avoids delegation altogether by reasoning that it's perfectly natural to:
- Do the job myself because it seems quicker and easier.
- Do it myself so I know it will be right.
- Keep a close check on the progress of a project since I have the experience and can speed up completion.

- Spell out in complex detail how subordinates should accomplish the task.

A variety of behaviors can be related to the delegation process, but not all of them necessarily lead to effective delegation. For example, a superior can turn a task over to a subordinate and then abdicate from any personal involvement, or at the other extreme, the leader may transfer authority and then over-supervise the follower. Therefore, it's necessary for leaders to learn effective delegation skills as well as to recognize the need to delegate as one moves up in a hierarchy.

DELEGATION BASICS

Definition. Delegation involves turning over enough authority and responsibility for doing a specific task to a subordinate who is held accountable for the performance of that task. What it boils down to is getting the tasks done through people. Delegation allows people to do the tasks they're trained to do. It occurs first at the direct supervisor level. The direct supervisor delegates work assignments to the doers. At this level, called the lowest level of supervision, the direct supervisor implements higher headquarters instructions or instructions from higher levels of management. As we move higher up in the management level, the supervisor is involved less with doing and more with using management techniques to steer the organization toward meeting its goals. These goals are met through the use of the management functions: planning, organizing, leading, and controlling.

Delegation is the practice of turning over to a subordinate enough authority to do a specific task, and then holding that person accountable for the results.

Vital Shift. As people move up the management ladder, they should shift from "doers" to "managers." This is called the vital shift. However, a problem experienced by many supervisors is that as they move up the management ladder, they actually increase the level of "doing" rather than the level of "managing." This is a result of our work ethic. Our society values hard work, thus resulting in the need to keep busy. The functions of management—planning organizing, leading, and controlling—aren't considered working by some. Consequently, many managers spend much time "doing" what they should be managing. They fail to delegate the "doing" work so the management functions can be accomplished. Many managers neglect the concept of vital shift.

The Vital Shift
As leaders move up the organizational ladder, they should shift from "doers" to "managers."

WHY IS DELEGATION IMPORTANT?

In your first job as a cadet officer, manager, or supervisor, you may have one or more subordinates working for you. Failure to delegate effectively may cause you to:
- Feel rushed and overworked.
- Neglect your own supervisory duties.

- Limit the growth potential of subordinates.
- Hamper your unit in accomplishing the mission with maximum operational effectiveness.

What are some of the benefits to be gained by practicing effective delegation? First, what does the supervisor gain? Simply stated, it gets you away from the activity trap and allows more time to plan. It enables you to observe not only the mission being accomplished, but permits visits to subordinates and supervisors in their working environment. You'll have more time to think through problems–to be creative and reflective. Additionally, since you'll have the responsibility of evaluating the work of subordinates, delegation won't only challenge these skills, but will provide the opportunity for a more equitable evaluation.

Now, what about the advantages to the subordinates? First, the officer, manager, or supervisor has an opportunity to become personally involved with his/her job and will probably grow from that experience. Next, delegation offers a great deal of latitude in determining the methods for getting the job done. This could very well tap an unsuspected reservoir of creativity. The officer, manager, or supervisor becomes exposed to the challenges of decision making and develops executive abilities. When you find persons who aren't decisive in key decision-making roles, it may be that they developed in an atmosphere of limited delegation practices.

The person who has been delegated a piece of the action and has the authority to manage resources will invariably be held in higher regard by subordinates. When the lieutenant delegates to the sergeant, it communicates to the sergeant and others in the organization that the lieutenant *trusts* the sergeant. In a word, the lieutenant's delegation gives the sergeant "clout!"

There's one other important benefit of good delegation practices, and that's that the organization itself benefits. Think about the overall payoff that flows to the work section, squadron, or wing. Not only is morale higher, but the overall managerial effectiveness of the organization is enhanced. There's more time for good planning, which improves the decision-making process. Fewer decisions are overtaken by events; more tasks are handled in proper time. There's usually a reduction of internal paperwork. Many jobs previously handled by the commander are now handled by lower level supervisors. Instead of a middle manager submitting written recommendations (with a lot of details that would be required by a high-level decision maker), the middle manager conducts his/her own analysis, makes the decision, implements it, and keeps the boss in the feedback loop.

Who Benefits from Delegation?

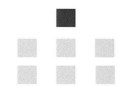

THE LEADER
- gains help in accomplishing the mission
- can focus efforts on other aspects of the mission
- develops followers into experts who may come to know more about a facet of the mission than the leader does

THE FOLLOWER
- enjoys an opportunity for personal growth
- finds job security by becoming the team's expert on a facet of the mission
- wins self-respect and the trust and respect of the team

THE TEAM
- taps a reservoir of creativity
- accomplishes more simply because delegation is a "force multiplier"
- makes better decisions because problems are handled systematically, all in due time

The delegation process lends itself to mutual goal setting, improved communications, demonstrated trust, recognition, and higher morale. Collectively, all these things lead to one of the more important qualities an organization can enjoy — TEAMWORK!

Yosemite
President Theodore Roosevelt (left) was one of America's great conservationists. So too was John Muir (right). Together they preserved the land that is now Yosemite National Park. The president had good sense enough not to get in Mr. Muir's way. Each leader supported the other in their mutual efforts to protect America's natural resources.

HOW TO USE DELEGATION EFFECTIVELY

As we mentioned before, delegation is the turning over of both authority and responsibility for doing a job to a subordinate who is held accountable for the performance of that job. In defining delegation, three key words are used: authority, responsibility, and accountability. These are very important concepts in the delegation process. A good delegator must realize what authority he/she has, what responsibility really means, and the importance of holding someone accountable.

Authority. Let's discuss the first concept in the delegation process— authority. A good definition of authority is, "that influence one possesses at any point in time, which will cause someone to do what the authoritative individual wants them to do at that time." Authority can come from many sources. Many times when we delegate a task to a subordinate, he/she inevitably asks, "How much authority will you give me?" The reason most bosses don't delegate authority of position to their subordinates is because of the risk involved.

Whenever a boss delegates total authority of position to a subordinate, he/she is taking the risk that the subordinate will misuse that authority. When this occurs, problems develop. Thus, many supervisors and managers are reluctant to delegate the authority of position to subordinates. Authority is an essential ingredient of the delegation process, permitting the delegation to be carried out. Regardless of the skill and thoroughness with which the preceding parts of the

"The best executive is the one who has sense enough to pick good people to do what he wants done, and self-restraint enough to keep from meddling with them while they do it." [84]

—THEODORE ROOSEVELT

delegation process have been handled, no delegation takes place if the subordinate isn't granted the authority to accomplish his/her goal. The authority required for effective delegation is characterized by several attributes:

- There must be a transfer of power from the superior to the subordinate.

- Authority must be specific enough for the subordinate to proceed without fear of exceeding his/her authority.

- Authority should be granted in advance, so the manager may plan his/her future course of action more effectively.

- Normally, authority should be delegated to the lowest organizational level where all information necessary for decision making and action come together, or is available.

- Above all, the degrees of authority must equal the extent of the subordinate's responsibility.

Responsibility. The next concept of delegation is responsibility. Just what's responsibility? Responsibility consists of the obligation to undertake a specific duty or task within the organization. When a person is made responsible for developing a policy or coming up with a plan, the boss who made that person responsible has delegated or assigned the task to the subordinate.

Recall that in chapter 10 (p. 75), we borrowed from an expert the definition of a manager as "someone who has responsibility for making a contribution." This section carries forward that definition of a manager.

Accountability. Accountability is another key concept in delegation. Accountability consists of assessing what and how a person did on a particular job (that is, were goals accomplished?). If a person has failed to do a job, that person has failed to develop and/or use the necessary authority, or that person hasn't shouldered the responsibility for accomplishing the job. Sometimes people don't accomplish their assigned task, or they accomplish it incorrectly. They always have an excuse, sometimes even a good excuse, for failing. But, good management principles, particularly those of effective delegation, hold a person accountable for failing to perform as required, irrespective of the reasons for that failure. It must be recognized that accountability is necessary for good delegation. If people aren't held accountable for failing to perform the work delegated to them, all discipline within the organization will be gone. *Many supervisors and managers fail to delegate effectively because they stop short of accountability.* They don't realize that accountability provides

"HECKUVA JOB, BROWNIE!"

Assuming that the federal response to the largest natural disaster in US history – Hurricane Katrina – was going well, President Bush commended FEMA Director Michael Brown (below, far right). "Brownie, you're doing a heckuva job," remarked the president.[85] Bush would later regret the praise.

In truth, Director Brown's performance was soon revealed to be abysmal. Accordingly, he resigned amidst widespread, bipartisan charges of incompetence.

The case study teaches two lessons. First, the boss cannot assume his lieutenants always do a great job. Delegation requires follow-up. Second, when a subordinate is delegated authority to act, with that authority comes accountability. And so, Brownie had to go.

the feedback necessary to tell whether or not the delegated work has been accomplished. Corrective action can't be taken by the managers if they don't know how or if the work has been performed.

One of the main reasons managers fail to make good work assignments and delegate effectively is they don't use accountability to provide them with feedback concerning the progress of the jobs they have assigned. When this is the case they're reluctant to delegate, usually preferring to do the job themselves to be sure it gets done.

STEPS FOR EFFECTIVE DELEGATION

Now let's combine the concepts of delegation into a sequential pattern to make it work for us.

Define the Task. The first step in the delegation process is to determine what tasks are suitable for delegation; not all tasks are suitable, as we'll find out. Here are some examples of tasks which may be delegated:

- Routine, repetitive details.

- Duties that make you over-specialized.

- Tasks your subordinates are more qualified to do.

- Tasks that add variety to subordinates' jobs.

- Duties that help create a "whole" job concept for your subordinates. Avoid delegating parts of a task, if possible.

Assign the Task. In this step of the process, we initially seek to integrate the concepts of responsibility, authority, and accountability in the subordinate. We do it in the following manner:

- Choose the right person for the task. There may be certain criteria we seek in individuals when a task needs to be delegated, so it pays to choose wisely!

- Explain the purpose of the job. The superior should thoroughly explain the job and organizational policies associated with the job, so the subordinate is knowledgeable on those responsibilities required of him/her.

- Explain goals, obtain commitment. In this manner, we can obtain the necessary accountability for effective delegation. The subordinate is aware of what his/her job's specific goals are and has pledged commitment towards meeting those goals.

- Encourage questions. You should, as a supervisor, encourage participation by your subordinates. By having an open, communicative style, ideas and problems can be discussed in a positive manner.

DELEGATION IN A NUTSHELL

1. Define the Task.

2. Assign the Task.

3. Grant Authority.

4. Follow Up.

Assigning the Task
Leaders need to take time to explain the purpose of the job and to describe what "success" looks like.

125

Grant Authority. A critical step of the delegation process is granting authority to the subordinate to accomplish the task or specific goal. There are degrees of authority, and it's a function of the level of training the subordinate has. An error many supervisors make is to grant a higher degree of authority than the subordinate can handle or is required for the task. Examples of degrees of authority, from low to high:

Granting Authority
The military rank system illustrates the principle that granting authority is a critical step of the delegation process. Higher ranking personnel have the authority to lead others in executing the mission.

- Look into the problem—report everything to superior so he/she can make the decision.

- Look into the problem—present the superior with a few alternatives; recommend one for his/her approval.

- Look into the problem—but don't take any action until you get the superior's approval.

- Look into the problem—let the supervisor know what you intend to do; do it unless he/she says no.

- Take action—let the supervisor know what you did.

- Take action—no further contact with the supervisor is necessary.

For different circumstances and different people you may use different degrees of delegation, but in all cases, subordinates need to know precisely what degree of authority you're giving them. Ideally, you as the superior should seek the highest level or degree of authority necessary for the subordinate to achieve his/her accountability towards the task. A key aspect is achieving this level, or degree of authority, in training. The superior must train his/her subordinate to use authority at its various levels or degrees.

Encourage Questions
Take the mystery out of delegated assignments. Encourage followers to ask questions and discuss their initial ideas with you so their work leads to success, not a dead end.

Follow Up. The remaining step in the delegation process is follow-up action. Controls and feedback channels must be established to ensure the delegated tasks have been accomplished and standards have been met. Also, this periodic feedback check of the quality of the work lets the workers know they're doing things right or wrong. Controls can be established by direct observation, quality controls, or progress reports. Some points to guide you include:

- Don't over-control subordinates. Don't smother employees by watching every little thing they do.

- Give positive feedback. Your subordinates need constructive comments to accomplish the task, and as the superior, you need to let them know.

- Be realistic. Don't bog your subordinates down in achieving stan-

Follow Up
The final step in the delegation process is the follow-up. Here, the boss checks that the job was completed to specification. (Most leaders see no need to follow up on minor, routine items assigned to proven performers.) This is also a time for positive, constructive feedback.

dards beyond their capabilities. As superiors, be concerned with "workable" solutions. You can cause more frustration in your subordinates when you demand unobtainable or difficult standards that go beyond "workable." This is the "Rolls-Royce" syndrome. It's nice to have the best solution to a task, but most people can fulfill the task with something less than the best. As superiors / supervisors you should encourage your subordinates to do their absolute best in all things, realizing that mistakes help them mature as followers.

- Have self-restraint. When a subordinate makes a mistake, as will definitely occur, will you get mad, blow up, or ignore it? None of these approaches is correct. When your follow-up uncovers a mistake, approach the subordinate with an attitude of, "It's normal to have some mistakes while learning. What can we do to correct the current mistake and prevent it from happening in the future?"

TRAINING SUBORDINATES TO ACCEPT DELEGATION

Junior officers need the freedom of movement only good delegation techniques can provide, by making use of qualified assistants who can take over whenever needed. When authority is granted to our assistants, the degree of authority given is a function of how much training subordinates have received to accomplish the tasks required. Ideally, the movement from telling a subordinate, "Look into the problem—report everything to me so I can make the decision," to "Take action—no further contact with me is necessary," requires the superior to involve the subordinate in a detailed and evolutional training program to eventually end up at the highest level of authority, which is, "Take action" by the subordinate. How do we do that? How do we develop our subordinates to accept the increasing degrees of delegation? Here are some rules to follow:

"Sir, i have everything under control. You may return to your donuts, erh, office, sir."

No "Helicopter" Bosses
Show self-restraint by giving followers enough time and space to complete a delegated assignment in their own way. Don't hover around them like a helicopter.

- Subordinates must be thoroughly briefed about what's happening and what's expected of them.

- The assistants should give the superior frequent progress reports. This is part of the controlling aspect which is essential to delegation. How does a good progress report assist a superior in the delegation process? First, it gives accurate information about the current status of jobs. Second, it compares the progress of jobs against current standards. Next, the report gives information on a timely basis to appropriate corrective action may be taken, if required. Finally, it should state what type of corrective action is needed.

- Superiors need to develop a sense of responsibility in their subordinates. This can be done by constantly giving them additional responsibilities and holding them accountable. These subordinates should be encouraged to seek out as much responsibility as they can handle.

- Lastly, the subordinates must be shown their supervisors can be trusted. Subordinates need to know their bosses will back them up when necessary. If subordinates trust their superiors, they'll realize criticism isn't personal but for the good of the organization. Subordinates will learn the value of constructive criticism.

PROBLEMS IN DELEGATION

What Delegation Isn't. We've just discussed what delegation is. Now let's talk about what delegation isn't. Many supervisors confuse delegation with abdication. Delegation isn't abdicating responsibilities. Abdication occurs when the boss lets the doer take care of the problem without proper training or clearly defined decision-making authority. That is, they simply dump jobs on the doers and then hold them accountable for the subsequent performance of those jobs while giving them little or no guidance. They are "passing the buck." Delegation is a different process. It is giving a problem to a subordinate who has been trained to make the decisions involving that problem.

Many supervisors are guilty of abdication. They give a subordinate a task only because they want to get rid of it. They do this in the manner of delegation, but it's really abdication.

Tasks That Shouldn't Be Delegated. Problems in delegation arise when we as superiors or supervisors assign the wrong task to subordinates. The following are tasks that shouldn't be delegated:

- Conceptual Planning – This is the responsibility of higher level supervisors and is the place where the functions of management are applied to steer the organization toward established goals and shouldn't be delegated to subordinates.

- Morale Problems – It's the responsibility of the supervisor, not the subordinate, to oversee the morale and welfare of an organization's people.

- Staff Problems – Higher management, not subordinates, needs to work these problems.

- Reviewing Subordinate Performance Reports – The process of reviewing subordinate performance reports shouldn't be delegated. An integral part of a supervisor's job is to assess the performance of subordinates. The supervisor is also the only person who should be qualified to make a true assessment of a person's performance.

- Specialized Tasks – Tasks that were given to a specific individual must not be delegated. Usually the supervisor has a good reason – training, development, or confidentiality – for making this request.

INESCAPABLE RESPONSIBILITY

The most important tasks cannot be delegated. Only the boss can perform them. Delivering a major announcement that affects the whole team is such an example.

(Top) President Clinton admits to having an affair with a White House intern. The relationship was "wrong," he said. "I misled people, and I deeply regret that."[86]

(Middle) President Obama delivers the good news that US troops located and killed Osama bin Laden.[87]

(Below) A speech which, thankfully, never was. President Nixon would have delivered this address to the world, if Apollo 11 had stranded Neil and Buzz on the Moon.[88]

None of these addresses could be delegated; each was too momentous.

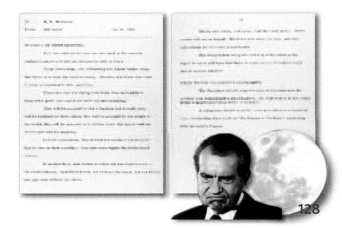

- Confidential Tasks – It's wrong to compromise the security of confidential information by exposing it to unauthorized persons.

- Pet Projects – This is a misuse of company time and resources and must not be delegated. Also, pet projects don't contribute to accomplishing the overall goals of an organization.

- Parts of a Problem – Parts of problems can't be delegated because of the difficulty in maintaining a standardization and consistency in solving the overall problem.

Why We As Superiors Fail to Delegate. Most of us don't delegate very much because of several fears. We'll discuss a few of the most common:

- Takes Too Much Time. We fear that, "It takes more time to show someone else how to do the job than to do it myself." This is probably true the first time or two you ask someone to do a job, but you should look upon delegation as an investment. The second or third time you ask a subordinate to do a job, you'll find it takes less time.

- Too Many Mistakes. We fear that, "If I delegate this task, the employee will not do it very well, and I'll look bad." The employee may not do the job as well as you can, especially the first few times. Try to reduce mistakes by delegating gradually, utilizing the steps in granting authority talked about before. Again, look upon this as an investment. Part of growing is making mistakes and learning from them. Allow your subordinates this privilege. They'll be better for it.

- Subordinates Show Me Up! We fear that, "If I delegate and my subordinate does a good job, it'll make me look bad." If your subordinates do well on a job, that is a mark of a good supervisor. People who get promoted rapidly have good, well-trained subordinates ready to step in. In general, job satisfaction is higher and complaints lower when supervisors delegate well.

- Lose Touch With the Job. We fear that, "If I delegate, I'll lose touch and wont' have the answers when my boss checks on how the job is coming along." You probably will lose touch with some details. That's part of the purpose of delegation.

You must be free of the detailed work so you can concentrate on the management functions, rather than on the "doing" tasks. Try to anticipate what questions your boss is likely to ask and structure your follow-up system to answer these questions. Don't be afraid to call your people in to answer your boss's request if you become stumped.

Common Mistakes in Delegation. Since delegation is a skill, we're likely to make mistakes. We can reduce our mistakes by being aware of the most common problems:

- Unclear Delegation. We fail to enumerate the key areas of responsibility, authority, or accountability. You need to be very specific

SIGNS OF INADEQUATE DELEGATION

- The office comes to a standstill when boss is gone.

- Very rugged treatment of anyone who makes mistakes; weeping over errors.

- General scarcity of promotables when vacancies occur.

- Little orientation to management objectives.

- Absence of stated performance standards for bosses.

- "Routineness" sets in.

- Bottlenecks remain and nothing is done about them.

- Backlog of good ideas that never get implemented

- Turnover rate is high.

- Inequitable work load between various levels of management.

- Deadlines missed fairly often.

- Lots of "firefighting" and crash programs.

- Key people very occupied with details.

- Decision making centered on one or a few people.

- Proposed changes, once installed, seem never to work.

- Excessive use of committees and task forces because committees splinter responsibilities.

- Limited interest in managerial succession.

- Lack of delegation skills in people who are promoted.

of tasking, degrees of authority, standards, deadlines, and follow-up.

- Supervise Too Closely. If you stand closely over your employee's shoulder looking for a mistake, he/she will likely make a mistake for you. This way of supervising takes too much time and builds resentment. Once you've delegated, turn loose—let them do the job they were trained to do.

- Helps Too Much. When you're explained a job well and assigned it to an employee, get out of the way! Frequently employees will come back to you after a few minutes and ask for help or want you to make a decision for them. Let them work out the details, if you've delegated the task to them effectively. The only way you're going to build their confidence level up is to allow them to work on the task themselves.

- Rushed Delegation. Plan delegation well in advance. Subordinates shouldn't be surprised when you leave for a trip, take a vacation, or receive a promotion. Prepare for emergencies by having tentative delegations in mind.

- Improper Selection of Subordinates. Some supervisors select subordinates who are incompletely trained for the job, and these people are given levels of authority far in excess of their abilities.

ORGANIZATIONAL CULTURE & CHANGE

Fine Print: Some experts use the terms "culture" and "climate" interchangeably, while others see climate as "a manifestation of culture."[90] For our purposes, climate and culture are one in the same.

Visit the USAF Thunderbirds at their home in Las Vegas and, immediately, words like precision, excellence, and honor come to mind. You see those qualities all around you. It's in the air. Everything at Thunderbird HQ is in its rightful place, just like the F-16s they fly in tight formations at high speed. The Thunderbirds' conference table is so well polished it gleams.

Precision & Spit-and-Polish
USAF Thunderbirds HQ

Visit one of Google's campuses anywhere around the world and you'll find "bicycles or scooters for efficient travel between meetings, dogs, lava lamps, massage chairs, and large inflatable balls."[89] Googlers, as they're called, say that they are so innovative because Google bosses make them comfortable about sharing ideas and opinions. The company is the opposite of stuffy. No one emphasizes title or rank – it's all about ability.

The paragraphs above describe organizations with two styles of excellence. The Thunderbirds and Google are world-class organizations, yet each gives off its own vibe, embracing its own unique culture. What is organizational culture?

Relaxed & Open
The Googleplex

ORGANIZATIONAL CULTURE

OBJECTIVE:

23. Define the term "organizational culture."

Organizational culture is "the commonly held values within a group of people."[91] Even more, "norms, customs, values, and assumptions that guide behavior" form the organizational culture of any team, company, school, or military unit.[92] Culture runs deep. It permeates the whole organization. If the Thunderbirds have a staff meeting, you just know it'll be a methodical, highly-organized affair. Meetings at Google surely must be free-form, with even low-ranking newcomers taking the conversation into new directions. In short, culture is "the way things are around here."[93]

Because culture is pervasive, any effort to transform an organization will result in mere tinkering around its edges, unless the leaders consider the organizational culture. For real change to stick, the culture has to change, too.[94] One expert explains why culture matters this way:

> *If we understand the dynamics of culture, we will be less likely to be puzzled, irritated, and anxious when we encounter the unfamiliar and seemingly irrational behavior of people in organizations, and we will have a deeper understanding not only of why various groups of people or organizations can be so different but also why it is so hard to change them.*[95]

Organizational culture explains the inexplicable. We glimpsed this principle in chapter 9 in the discussion of how the Air Force Symbol built a unifying sense of airmanship. In chapter 7, we studied a particular culture called the "learning organization," where everyone is constantly learning. We observed in chapter 3 that in America leaders succeed only if they respect our cultural heritage as a democracy. By studying organizational culture and its impact on leaders' efforts to change their teams and bring them to the next level of performance, "we will understand ourselves better and recognize some of the forces acting within us that define who we are."[96]

WHERE WOULD YOU PREFER TO GO TO SCHOOL?

No windows, so no natural light within. No flowers to add color or carry sweet fragrances. No trees for shade, and no places from where birds might sing. Even the door is puny.

Is this uninviting, sterile building (above) a warehouse? A prison? Actually, it's a middle school.

In the judgment of one social critic, the building "expresses to perfection our current social consensus about the meaning of education. It stares balefully at the street with the blank-faced demeanor of a [troubled] child preparing to explode in violent rage. It summarizes our collective aspirations about school as the unidentifiable contents of an inscrutable set of boxes."[97]

For all we know, this school could provide a world-class education. But what sense of the organization's culture do you get upon first glance? Would the sight of this campus make you excited about learning?

The University of Virginia campus (below) reflects its founder's sensibilities. Thomas Jefferson believed in a vibrant life of the mind. For him, learning was a lifelong endeavor, a shared journey toward universal truth.

Therefore, Jefferson's campus centers upon a Lawn, a physical and spiritual center where historians and poets, musicians and physicists, might encounter one another. Well-proportioned buildings frame this space, creating a sense of community. Atop The Lawn stands The Rotunda, a temple of knowledge in the style of the Roman Pantehon.

Jefferson knew that the design of the campus and the style of its buildings would signal the aspirations he had for his university, its faculty, and the young people who studied there. The University of Virginia is a world-class center of learning. No one could possibly mistake it for a warehouse or a prison. Even a casual visitor will immediately sense an organizational culture marked by free inquiry, community, and pride.

THE LEADER'S TOUGHEST JOB: CHANGING ORGANIZATIONAL CULTURE

OBJECTIVES:

24.   Name the three phases in leading organizational culture change.
25.   Define two challenges that can occur during the unfreezing phase of culture change.
26.   List and briefly define eight principles to consider during the learning phase of culture change.
27.   Identify four challenges to overcome during the internalization phase of culture change.

The ancient philosopher Heraclitus observed, "Character is destiny."[98] For organizations, that maxim translates to "culture is destiny." A group's commonly held values will define what it is capable of becoming. Therefore, leaders will want to shape their organization's culture, and if the old culture impedes future success, change it. How do leaders do that? The process of leading organizational culture change consists of three phases.[99]

UNFREEZING: CREATING THE MOTIVATION TO CHANGE

Phase one in the process of cultural change is called unfreezing because the organization is letting go of hard traditions and experiencing a motivation to change.

Survival Anxiety. Within this phase, the first step is the experience of "survival anxiety." Unless the team changes, something awful will happen. The team is beginning to realize this fact, and they don't like it. Fortunately, the silver lining to this grey thundercloud is that unpleasant feeling. Anxiety provides the energy for the team to change.

What causes survival anxiety? Someone has to douse the organization with that cold bucket of water called reality, to shock the system. The organization must experience disequilibrium, the uncomfortable feeling one gets when things that were in balance and harmony begin to wobble and collapse. A traumatic event triggers survival anxiety.

Until 9/11, not many Americans concerned themselves with the threat posed by terrorism. Yet, al-Qaida had attacked U.S. targets several times.[100] In 1993, al-Qaida bombed the World Trade Center, causing some damage and killing six people. Despite some counterterrorism experts' warnings, we went on with our lives as usual. Al-Qaida attacked two U.S. embassies in African countries in 1998, killing more than 200 and wounding more than 4,000. Again, a small number of experts tried to awaken us to the growing threat, with little noticeable effect. In 2000, al-Qaida bombed the U.S.S. *Cole*, killing 17 sailors and

Survival Anxiety
Al-Queda attacked the USS *Cole* (top), but that event did not cause most Americans to consider terrorism as a national priority. Then 9/11 came (bottom) and the events of that awful day were so dramatic that the U.S. knew it had to "unfreeze" and change its posture toward terrorism.

injuring 39. Still, we lacked motivation to make counterterrorism a national priority. Then 9/11 happened. That traumatic event finally triggered survival anxiety. At last, we knew our inattentiveness toward terrorism had to change. We made that change, and it was painful indeed.

Unlearning. To unfreeze or get the team unstuck will require unlearning. Bad habits must die. The old mindset and old way of doing things must be forgotten or unlearned.

If you've ever watched someone struggle to quit smoking, you have some idea of how tough unlearning can be. Remember, in speaking of organizational culture, we're speaking of values that permeate the organization. Bad culture can't simply be washed away with a garden hose; the team's values, attitudes, assumptions, and ways of getting the job done are dyed in the wool. Therefore, even though the behavior is dysfunctional, it's hard to give up. Smokers have to unlearn the idea that being comfortable requires them to have a cigarette between their fingers. Alcoholics have to unlearn the idea that booze is a prerequisite for fun. Organizations have to unlearn their old ways of doing business. Leaders who try to change organizational culture are in for a very tough ride.

A Tough Habit to Kick

To quit smoking, you have to unlearn the habit. Overcoming the nicotine addiction is only part of the story. You have to unlearn the desire to have something in your hands, and unlearn the desire to smoke simply to pass the time while driving, for example. In changing a team's culture, leaders need to help the team unlearn the old behaviors.

LEARNING NEW CONCEPTS

Now that the organization is motivated to change, phase two begins. Here, the organization's leaders help people learn the new concepts that will bring the desired culture into effect.

Clear Articulation of Vision. Although the organization experienced survival anxiety, senior leaders must describe the organization's predicament with clarity and precision. What exactly is the threat? What is our current situation? Articulating that reality provides a context for change and ensures that everyone is aware of the threat. Further, the leadership team must articulate their vision for the future. What, specifically, does the new future look like? Official statements delivered by the boss are essential. These statements may take the form of open letters to the team, special announcements published in writing, a keynote address at a special assembly, or any means that signals a major break from routine.

Psychological Safety. The whole process of learning new concepts and embracing the new culture needs to be as positive as possible. A degree of psychological safety is required. "The learner must come to feel that

The SECDEF Leads a Cultural Change

As you read Secretary Panetta's announcement that the "Don't Ask, Don't Tell" law that barred homosexuals from military service is no longer in effect, notice how the Pentagon had been carefully planning for that major change. Leaders provided training so that everyone would understand the new cultural norms and expectations.

"Last December, [the Pentagon] began a careful and methodical process to prepare for the repeal of 'Don't Ask, Don't Tell.

"Since then, the Repeal Implementation Team has worked to coordinate the necessary changes to policy and regulations, and to provide training to service members.

"Today, as a result of strong leadership and proactive education throughout the force, we can take the next step in this process. [We hereby certify] that the implementation of repeal of 'Don't Ask, Don't Tell' is consistent with [military] standards."[101]

SECRETARY LEON PANETTA

the new way of being is possible and achievable, and that the learning process itself will not be too anxiety-provoking or demeaning."[102]

Consider CAP's transition to "glass cockpits," the GPS-enabled, digital flight instruments that are replacing the old steam gauges throughout general aviation. Experienced pilots might fear the change. "I was an expert with steam gauges, now I'm a rookie." "What if I make a fool of myself?" "What if I can't make the mental transition to glass?" "If I mess up, will I be punished? Injured?" These are psychological fears affecting individuals' sense of identity and prestige.

Smart leaders know that if they recognize fears and provide support, their people will feel a helpful sense of psychological safety.

C-172 "Steam Gauges"

C-172 "Glass Cockpit"

The Right Metrics & Rewards. What's measured tends to be what gets done. To effect cultural change, leaders rethink how they measure success in their organization, and they ensure the reward systems (pay, awards, promotions, atta-boys) are aligned with those new metrics. Consider the job of the grocery store stock clerk. What matters more, stocking the shelves or helping the customer? Here comes a customer in search of pignolia nuts. If shelf-stocking is the metric, the clerk says, "Lady, they're in aisle 3," and keeps on stocking. If service matters most, the clerk escorts the customer to aisle 3, stops halfway down on the right, reaches toward the top shelf, and says, "Here are your pignolia nuts, ma'am. Can I help you with anything else?" Whatever goal is desired, the metrics and rewards must be properly aligned. One expert puts it this way: "Restructure the rewards and sanctions to make them consistent with the new priorities, goals, and values. Reinforce the behavior you want."[103] Leaders need to make clear what they will be monitoring, ignoring, measuring, and controlling.[104]

Symbols & Physical Environment. Effective symbols are visual representations of reality. Once again, the story of the Air Force symbol providing a sense of service-wide unity is relevant. So, too, is the story of IBM's "think" motto in chapter 5. And the comparison of the prison-like middle school with the university campus suggestive of ancient Greece and Rome, made earlier in this chapter, shows how physical environment sets a tone that affects culture. However, the physical environment may be impractical to change, and symbols and slogans are ripe for mockery. Consider the short-lived slogan that the U.S. Army adopted in 2001, "An Army of One." The intention was to

Change in the Cockpit
Flying is flying, but if you are an older pilot, or someone who simply has difficulty transitioning from one system to another, switching to a glass cockpit might be daunting.

Good Metrics, with Psychological Safety
The purpose of metrics is to "make self control possible," not to arm managers with a stick with which to beat the workforce. According to the humanizing view of Peter F. Drucker, metrics should not be "weapons of internal secret police."[105] As the organization transforms its culture and realigns its metrics, leaders ought to stay positive and provide "psychological safety."

champion the power of the individual and promote a culture where soldiers strive to be their best. But read that slogan with a snarky attitude, and its meaning is transformed or "deconstructed." One social critic observed that the slogan "represents a stunning reversal of attitude . . . respect from others [had been] more important than respect for yourself."[106] If an army is anything, it is a team, and yet the slogan suggested the primacy of the individual over the team.

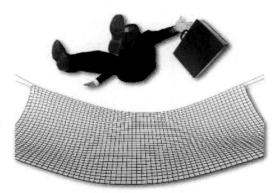

Safety Nets
Leaders need to commit resources to training people so they can meet the new standards and display the new cultural norms. That training and transitory period is like a safety net.

Training & Safety Nets. Although they have worked hard to unlearn the old, bad behaviors, team members still must learn the new behaviors, skills, and attitudes that the new culture demands. Therefore, leaders have to commit resources to training people so that they can make the change.

Time for learning, coaches to teach new skills, (metaphorical) practice fields where people can learn in a supportive environment, and helpful feedback are all necessary.[107] Throughout this learning process, team members rightfully have a say in *how* they will meet the organization's new cultural expectations. However, the fact that the organization *is* making a change and *shall* transform itself is not open for debate.[108] One expert suggests a tough-love approach: "Be willing to sacrifice those people whose attitude and behavior could sabotage the culture change. Better to lose them than to put the whole organization's survival at risk."[109] But, in a volunteer environment like CAP, tough-love tactics can do much more harm than good.

General Curtis LeMay
Did Gen LeMay, the legendary commander of Strategic Air Command, really fire the base commander and promote the sentry on the spot? Does it matter?

Stories to Communicate Culture. Push a car tire into upscale clothing store Nordstrom's, ask for a refund, and you'll get your money back. No matter that Nordstrom's doesn't sell tires![110] In the literal sense, Nordstrom probably does not issue many tire refunds, but Nordstrom executives encourage the exaggeration because it dramatically makes a point. Nordies (the name employees call themselves) are empowered to use their good judgment in satisfying the customer. Anecdotes have power. Stories help people learn. According to Air Force lore, General Curtis LeMay was inspecting a base. Local commanders had been told to watch for the general's car to come zipping through the gate at a certain moment of a particular day. Sentries at the gate were to let the general through without stopping to check IDs. Somehow, the airman at the gate did not receive those instructions. When Gen. LeMay's car barreled onto the base without stopping, this airman (so the story goes) shot out the car's tires and face-planted Gen. LeMay and his driver onto the asphalt, hands cuffed behind their backs. When the dust settled, Gen. LeMay fired the base commander for not passing along the instructions, but promoted the airman to sergeant on the spot. Did it really happen? Does it matter? If you worked for Gen. LeMay, you'd know that you had better

pass along orders without fail. You'd also know that if you zealously enforced standard procedure, no one would ever second-guess you. A story conveys the organization's culture.

Teachable Moments. As leaders attempt to change organizational culture and usher in new attitudes and expectations, experts say that they should be on the lookout for "teachable moments." A teachable moment is simply an unplanned opportunity enabling a leader to emphasize a principle that someone (or a group of people) have been trying to learn. Suppose you are trying to cultivate a safety-minded culture in your squadron. You've provided formal training in operational risk management (ORM) and mentioned the importance of imagining worst-case scenarios so that you can avoid them or at least plan for them. A week or two after teaching ORM, you hear that a cadet ran out of fuel while driving on the highway. She was miles from a gas station and had forgotten her cell phone. That real-life occurrence presents a teachable moment, an opportunity to re-emphasize what you had been saying about ORM and really bring that point home.

Leadership By Example. Finally, culture change, like so much else in the field of leadership, requires leadership by example. Leaders must model those behaviors they wish to see in others. Normally, when discussing leadership, the first principle people mention is "lead by example." In a discussion of culture change, it is appropriate to save it for last because one individual leader's personal example is likely to be insufficient in changing the values, attitudes, behaviors, and standards of an entire organization. Vision, psychological safety, metrics and rewards, symbols, environment, training, stories, and teachable moments – a good mix of tools – are needed to effect cultural change at the organization level. Still, no change is possible without leaders modeling the desired behaviors.

INTERNALIZATION: OWNING THE NEW CULTURE

On New Year's Day, millions of people go on a diet. By Groundhog Day, most have given up. These would-be dieters realized the need for change or "unfreezing" via phase one of the cultural change process. Many of them worked hard to learn and acquire new concepts, perhaps by exercising and watching what they ate – phase two. Still, the diet failed. The new culture didn't stick.

Leadership by Example
There is no substitute for the leader's personal, visible commitment to cultural change. You've got to be out in front.

Characteristics of Lasting Commitments. Phase three of the organizational cultural change process involves internalization. Simply stated, internalization is what results when someone makes a lasting commitment to a principle. That commitment becomes almost second nature. People who have internalized a commitment to the Core Values, for example, not only parrot the definitions of those values, but if given a choice to show integrity or its opposite, they <u>freely choose</u> integrity. If excellence is challenged, they will <u>justify</u> or <u>defend</u> it. When mentoring a new cadet, those who have internalized the Core Values will <u>invite</u> that newcomer to follow their lead. Notice that the <u>underlined words</u> are robust action verbs.[111] Cultural change will not truly take root without the deep commitment called internalization.

If individuals find it difficult to manage their personal cultural change, as so many frustrated dieters do, imagine how much more daunting it is for leaders to see an entire organization's cultural change through to its conclusion.

Out With the Old Behavior. In leading cultural change, the *individual team members* do not necessarily need to change, but their *behavior* does.[112] Ideally, no one is fired. However, everyone on the team must demonstrate through their actions a sustained commitment to the new standards and way of doing business. Veteran members of the team must change their behavior to remain with the team. By ceasing with the old, undesirable behavior, veterans display a sign of internalization. Likewise, adherence to the new culture is the new person's price of admission to the team.

Need for Success. One expert found that, "Old cultural elements can be destroyed by eliminating the people who 'carry' those elements, but new cultural elements can only be learned if the new behavior leads to success and satisfaction."[113] In other words, the new cultural norms have to make the team "better." The team must "win," if the new culture is to stick and be internalized. Therefore, leaders should

Change & Commitment
Internalization – the act of making a lasting commitment – is like the old joke about ham and eggs. The chicken is merely *involved*. But the pig, he's *committed*.

THE METRIC SYSTEM'S LONG, SLOW DEMISE

If teams need incremental success to make change stick, does that mean cultural change should be a long, drawn-out affair? The evidence suggests the opposite.

In 1975, the U.S. Congress enacted a statement of federal policy whereby we would become a metric nation by 1992.[114] Americans would have a generous seventeen years to gradually switch to the unfamiliar metric system.

By that time, highway signs would announce distance to the next city in kilometers. Weather forecasters would give temperatures in Celsius. Your identification cards would report your height in centimeters, your weight in kilograms.

Obviously that did not happen. Right or wrong, people resisted the change. The long, drawn-out period of transition did not make cultural change

more likely, but rather helped the naysayers win through attrition.

Efforts at change do need to collect small wins along their march to final victory. But in the judgment of one cultural change expert, lasting change is not so much a matter of incremental victories, but a fast-moving snowball effect.

"Deliver hard results in a hurry, and you buy some time for culture change to build momentum."[115]

take a graduated approach to the change, moving toward full compliance over a reasonable period of time. As the team successfully reaches those milestones, team leaders can celebrate those successes with the team and reward the rank-and-file troops who helped lead the transformation.[116]

Adversaries of Change. If change were easy, everyone would welcome it. Emerson's claim that "a foolish consistency is the hobgoblin of little minds,"[117] mentioned back in chapter 5 in the context of creative thinking, speaks of resistance to change being something like a default setting in most individuals. One management expert states the obvious: "Disaffected employees will undermine their managers' credibility and well-designed plans."[118]

Change disrupts the troops' routine. In turn, some individuals reply by being disruptive in their own right. Why? Change seems to violate an unspoken social compact.[119] "I do the job I was hired to do, and the company leaves me alone." But jobs change. Second, the law of inertia suggests that frustrated individuals can wait out the change attempt. In the federal government, for example, political appointees lead federal agencies for terms of less than four years, on average. Career civil servants may display an attitude of, "I was here before you and your change program, and I'll still be here when you're gone." Third, to the potential for general resistance, add the fact that no manager understands a job as well as the incumbent. Veteran members of the team can be enormously knowledgeable about their field and the organization's business. Consequently, they are capable of nitpicking attempts at change (versus first engaging the issues at the strategic level). In short, disruptive behavior is an obvious sign that the new cultural norms have not been internalized.

The Nuclear Option. Change is impossible, in the words of one expert, "unless managers and subordinates throughout the organization are committed to the change."[120] Some experts argue that leaders can and should work with those individuals who hesitate in the face of change, but those who attempt

A Graduated Approach to Change
Hikers set intermediate goals before summiting. Likewise, in cultural change, the team needs to collect a few quick "wins" for the change to become internalized.

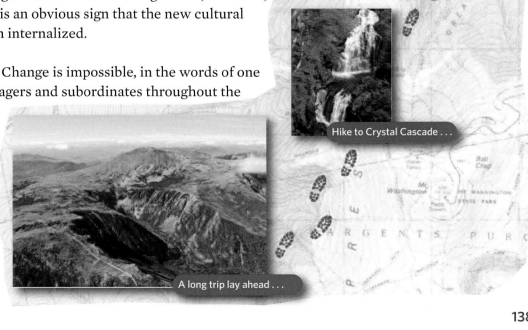

Bag the summitt . . . *done!*

Cross the Alpine Garden . . .

Get atop the headwall . . .

Into Tuckerman Ravine . . .

Hike to Crystal Cascade . . .

A long trip lay ahead . . .

to sabotage the effort or steadfastly refuse to change cannot be tolerated. The nuclear option is in order: termination or involuntary reassignment. Hard-core naysayers "will soak up most of your time, and still be an obstacle to the change effort," advises one expert. "You're better off (and they probably are, too) if you get rid of them . . . [or] position them where they will do the least damage."[121] Yet the "nuclear option" runs contrary to a positive approach to leadership. No wonder that changing the organizational culture is arguably the toughest job a leader will face.

LEADERSHIP FOR SAFETY

OBJECTIVES:

28. Identify four pillars for safety leadership.
29. Recall practical ways to develop a pro-safety organizational culture.

Safety is a function of organizational culture.[122] Unwritten rules, the way people act as a matter of fact, in spite of what they say they believe, have an enormous impact on whether a team keeps itself safe. One expert says it plainly: "Safety culture is how the organization behaves when no one is watching."[123]

SAFETY & THE COMMANDER

What is the commander's role in organizational safety? The first requirement of command, according two Navy admirals, is to ensure your people are safe so that they can perform the mission.[124] Beyond an initial status check or preflight, the leader's challenge is cultural. What is the team's current attitude toward safety? Is that organizational culture truly pro-safety? If not, what needs to be done to lead the team toward a positive safety attitude?[125]

FOUR PILLARS FOR SAFETY LEADERSHIP

What principles should guide commanders in their quest to develop a positive safety culture? Experts identify four basic pillars for safety leadership.[126]

Safety Must Be Integrated. If you're building an airplane, you can't merely check for quality at the end of the assembly line. By then it's too late. You have to look at quality every step of the way. Quality is integrated into the process. Likewise, safety also must be integrated into everything an organization does. Will the equipment your team purchases contribute to safety? As you change your work environment, perhaps moving calisthenics to the morning instead of after dinner at encampment, what effect will that have upon safety? Do you have ways to identify safety hazards, and does everyone know they can

CHERNOBYL

UKRAINE, 1986. The Chernobyl nuclear reactor explodes. Over 100 radioactive elements shoot into the atmosphere. The fire kills only two people at first, but hundreds develop fatal cancers over time. An area the size of Michigan is contaminated. All told, the Chernobyl disaster was 400 times more potent than the atomic bomb dropped on Hiroshima.[127]

But one good thing comes out of this horrible event. Safety experts begin looking beyond immediate engineering and technical failures when analyzing accidents. They start to consider safety's human side, the psychology of why people behave as they do, and the social factors that shape beliefs and attitudes toward safety.[128]

The workers at the Chernobyl reactor did not take safety seriously. Keeping the team safe is not just a matter of technology – the thickness of the steel around a reactor's core, the anti-lock capabilities of a car's brakes, the computerized terrain warning systems in airplanes. Individual and collective attitudes toward safety are also important.

Fine Print: A lesson on leadership for safety properly belongs under the heading, "Command Responsibility." Keeping the troops safe is a commander's sacred trust. We are placing this section here, following a discussion on organizational culture, because you will first need to understand what culture is before you can appreciate the commander's role as a leader for safety.

and must speak up when they see something wrong? Leaders have to find opportunities for the team to consider safety, and ensure team members have the time and resources to stay safe every step of the way.

Safety is a Right. Everyone in the organization has to buy into the understanding that safety is a basic right. Sure, there will always be risks in any job, but they must be managed responsibly. Sinclair Lewis's novel, *The Jungle,* depicted the horrors of the early 20th century industrial workplace. His descriptions of the Chicago stock-yards so infuriated readers that Congress was pressured to pass the *Pure Food and Drug Act* of 1906 – less than six months after the book was first published.[129] The law was an important first step in making leaders responsible for safety in their organizations. A sampling of *The Jungle's* horrors:

The book that alerted America to the dangers to its food supply and callously unsafe working conditions in the meat-packing industry. Sinclair's work sparked a new emphasis on safety and sanitation

> The meat would be shoveled into carts, and the man who did the shoveling would not trouble to lift out a rat even when he saw one . . . There was no place for the men to wash their hands before they ate their dinner, and so they made a practice of washing them in the water that was to be ladled into the sausage . . . There were some jobs that it only paid to do once in a long time, and among these was the cleaning out of the waste barrels . . . In the barrels would be dirt and rust and old nails and stale water—and *cartload after cartload of it would be taken up and dumped into the hoppers with fresh meat, and sent out to the public's breakfast.*[130] [emphasis added]

Everyone is Responsible for Safety. The price of admission to a safety-minded team is a willingness to accept responsibility for protecting one's own and the team's safety. The principles of systems thinking discussed back in chapter 7 come into play. No one member of the team can ensure the whole team remains safe. The interplay

An early 1900's illustration of the meatpacking industry, including its many safety and sanitation problems, during Sinclair's day. This depiction might be said to demonstrate a total lack of leadership for safety.

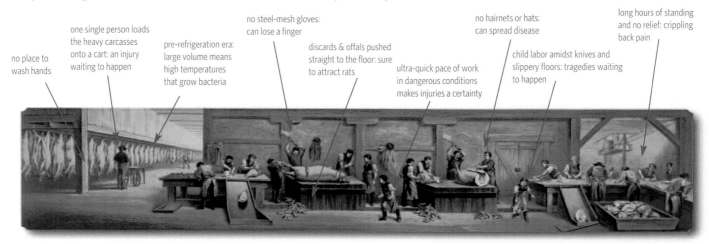

no place to wash hands

one single person loads the heavy carcasses onto a cart: an injury waiting to happen

pre-refrigeration era: large volume means high temperatures that grow bacteria

no steel-mesh gloves: can lose a finger

discards & offals pushed straight to the floor: sure to attract rats

ultra-quick pace of work in dangerous conditions makes injuries a certainty

no hairnets or hats: can spread disease

child labor amidst knives and slippery floors: tragedies waiting to happen

long hours of standing and no relief: crippling back pain

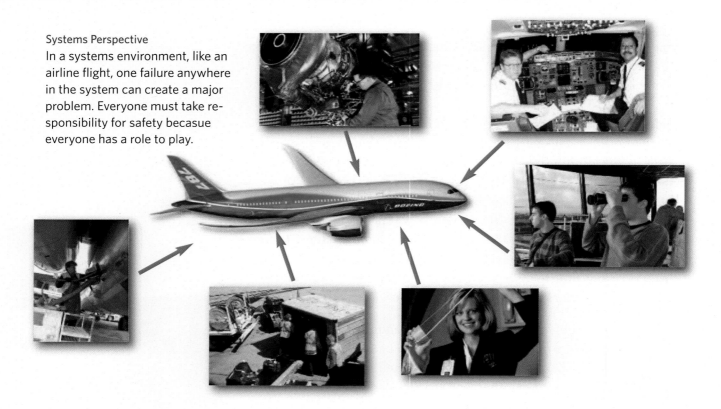

between individuals affects the whole system. Take a commercial airline for example. Ground crews carefully prepare the aircraft. Flight attendants brief the passengers and double-check the cabin. The pilot and co-pilot work through their preflight checklists, and the tower ensures the runway and departure area are safe before clearing the flight for take-off. We see safe habits on display all around. But if the maintenance mechanic chose not to check the torque on some hard-to-reach bolts, everyone else's attentiveness is for naught. Everyone must take responsibility for safety because everyone has a role to play.[131] One failure by a single individual can trigger a system-wide failure.

Safety is a Value. Do the Core Values ever change? No. The whole point is that those values endure. Perhaps somebody will rephrase them, but the basic values are timeless and universal. If leaders want their organizations to maintain pro-safety attitudes and behaviors at all times, they must treat safety as a value, too. In contrast, mere priorities change based on the needs of the organization. Today's priority may be to cut costs. Tomorrow's is to upgrade our technology. Next week our priority is customer service. As the situation changes, so do our priorities, and rightly so. Leaders who declare that safety is a value, and explain what that idea really means, send a message that safety is important and can't be compromised.[132]

DEVELOPING A PRO-SAFETY CULTURE

Safety requires the commander's leadership, and a pro-safety culture stands upon four pillars. But in practical terms, how do you go about developing a safety-minded organization?

Incentives. Perhaps incentives will work. If a team stays accident-free for a year, they earn some kind of incentive – a cash bonus, prestigious award, extra days off, etc. That approach is as ineffective as it is legally suspect.[133] Imagine a pilot who goofs the final approach. He makes a rough landing. A responsible airman will report that. What if the aircraft was damaged? It needs to get checked out. But might that pilot keep quiet? If he reports the mishap, his unit will lose its safety award. Therefore, incentives must encourage good behavior, not penalize bad behavior.[134] Catch people doing things right. If every member of the ground team has a compass and whistle, upon being spot checked by the first sergeant, for example, that team qualifies for the safety award or an incentive of some kind. The transportation officer places a small coupon on a van's spare tire. It reads, "Thank you for checking the air on the spare. Present this coupon for a small gift." Suggest a good idea for how to keep your team safe, and you qualify for some kind of perk. Incentives are effective motivators, but only if the program is based on positive reinforcement.

Trait Theory. In chapter 3, we discussed how early students of leadership simply watched good leaders in action to learn what leadership is. Likewise, we can learn fundamentals of safety leadership by studying the traits of leaders whose organizations have great safety records. Safety-minded leaders:[135]

- Help solve problems and fix safety hazards, instead of fixing blame

- Train their people how to do the job safely

- Provide the time, money, and equipment that people need to do their jobs safely

- Encourage people to report and discard broken and unsafe equipment, and back them up

- Actively seek input from the troops, even the lowest-ranking and least experienced members

- Publicly recognize pro-safety attitudes and behaviors

- Practice "no fear reporting" by banning managers from retaliating against people who raise safety concerns

- Empower everyone, everywhere to command "All Stop!" upon noticing a safety hazard

- Lead by example – personally comply with all safety rules, all the time

Once again, organizational culture is simply "the way things are around here." Commanders create the conditions for pro-safety attitudes and behaviors and foster a safety-minded culture, day in and day out. Merely tacking a "Be Safe" poster to the wall amounts to an abrogation of leadership responsibility.

HOW DO PRO-SAFETY LEADERS SUPPORT THEIR PEOPLE?

Encourage people to submit safety ideas

Train people how to be safe

Empower everyone to command, "STOP!"

Empower everyone to lock-out unsafe equipment

Provide safety equipment

Reward safe behaviors

Lead by example

MEASURING FOR SUCCESS

"Count what is countable,
measure what is measurable,
and what is not measurable,
make measurable."

GALILEO[136]

Among the responsibilities of command that cannot be delegated is the duty to ensure the team is pointed in the right direction. Leaders take bearings, mark a course, and track the team's movements across a map. Our common sense understanding of the infinitive, "to lead," is to physically bring someone to a new place. You cannot lead if you are unsure where you are going and how far you are from your intended destination. In this section, we consider how leaders measure success, first in regard to how well individual members of the team are performing, and second in how well the organization as a whole is fulfilling its aims.

MEASURING INDIVIDUAL PERFORMANCE

OBJECTIVES:
30.   Define the term "performance appraisal."
31.   Discuss advantages and drawbacks of using top-down performance appraisals.
32.   Describe the characteristics of 360-degree feedback.

PERFORMANCE APPRAISALS

The classic example of measuring individual performance is the annual performance appraisal. A performance appraisal is the process of measuring how well an individual has fulfilled assigned duties and responsibilities.[137] In some organizations, how well one scores on a performance appraisal can determine promotion prospects, annual bonuses, annual raises, and the like.

Philosophy of Appraisal. In a performance appraisal, the boss is in control. He or she communicates to team members or employees whether they are meeting expectations in terms of job performance. Organizations might soften this top-down flow of information by including some form of individual self-assessment, but the basic premise of a performance appraisal is that management communicates observed successes and shortcomings to each worker on an individual basis. The boss lets the underlings know where they stand.[138]

Reference to Standards. To measure performance, obviously some kind of yardstick or standard is needed. As mentioned earlier, a well-

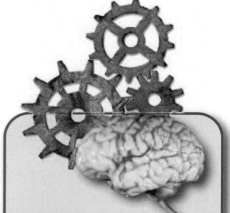

Appraising a Leader's Performance

Knowledge workers are people who work mostly with information or develop and use knowledge on the job. They are contrasted with manual workers.

A manual worker knows what is to be done. "I have to bag my customers' groceries, all day long." If you're a bagger at a grocery store, the job is obvious.

In knowledge work, the what is not clear. In fact, the job begins with the knowledge worker asking, "What should I do?"[139]

A squadron cadet commander, for example, draws upon his or her expertise in deciding if recruiting should be the unit's top priority, or perhaps training, or maybe developing new weekend activities. The what is the job's big mystery.

Consequently, it is more difficult to evaluate a knowledge worker's than a manual worker's performance on the job.

developed job description will be a source for those standards. The classic example is known as the "stopwatch standard."[140] Did the team member/employee manufacture 100 widgets per hour? But in the 21st century economy, a growing number of people are knowledge workers and service providers. Their work does not lend itself to stopwatch standards. Few people find themselves in robot-like jobs so easily measured. If your job involves creative thinking, problem solving, or satisfying a customer, it can be difficult to find an objective standard against which to measure your performance. One expert counters that while precise standards are hard to find, clear, well understood (though imprecise) standards should not be.[141] The attitude here is that the supervisor observes the employee and notes whether that individual "warmly greeted the customer," or whether he or she completed the project in a "reasonable amount of time."

Management by Objective. The search for relevant standards points some experts toward a concept called management by objective, or MBO. The basic idea is that "performance in each position is measured in relation to the objectives of the person and those of the organization."[142] Informed by the organization's long-term goals, the boss and subordinate agree upon a set of objectives – meaningful accomplishments the subordinate is expected to achieve within a period of time. These objectives may be tangible, "build a house by July 1st," or effects-based, "increase the cadet corps by 10%." The performance appraisal becomes a venue for evaluating if the subordinate fulfilled the agreed-upon objectives. We'll discuss MBO in more depth later in this chapter.

Weaknesses of Performance Appraisals. For boss and subordinate alike, a performance appraisal is often a socially awkward, unpleasant experience. Critics of performance appraisals argue that it amounts to a game of "Gotcha!"[143]* The boss is empowered to "hammer" the underling in a way that may satisfy the sadist, but is unlikely to help the subordinate improve. Moreover, by virtue of the appraisal being a boss-led exercise, the process contains a single-rater bias.[144] That is, the overall assessment depends upon just one person's judgment, making fairness and broadmindedness hard to achieve. Further, performance appraisals not only reflect upon the subordinate, the purported subject, but reflect upon the boss/rater as well. "I am a good boss, so my team members deserve good ratings," and the reverse, "If I rate this subordinate poorly, that shows I am doing a poor job leading her."[145] No wonder that many experts contend that performance appraisal systems often do not work as they are supposed to.[146]

* Excuse the crudeness, but the no-kidding technical term here is NIGYSOB, "Now I got you, son of a b%#ch!"[147]

Stopwatch Standard
The classic example of a performance measurement is the stopwatch standard. Did the employee make 100 widgets per hour? That's a straightforward standard. The problem with stopwatch standards is that they don't have much applicability to knowledge work.

MILITARY PERFORMANCE APPRAISALS:
USEFUL TOOL OR SHAM?

It's the key document affecting an officer's promotion. The Officer Performance Report (OPR), and its sibling, the Enlisted Performance Report (EPR), purportedly assesses an individual's performance on the job. But numerous web-based aids suggest that the actual ratings marked on OPRs are disingenuous. Any officer who does not receive "firewall 5's" (the highest possible rating) in all categories is to be considered a lackluster officer. "Any markdown on the front of the OPR is the kiss of death."[148]

OPRs and EPRs are often written in a code that makes the evaluated individual sound good on the surface, but those in the know get the intended message. "You can say just about anything you want about someone," advises the independent website," Air Force Writer, "but if you haven't qualified the statement by comparing him or her against their peers, you might as well not say anything at all. This is a great way of disguising your intent if your aim is to produce an ineffective EPR." Among the remarks suggested for 4th-tier performers, the bottom of the barrel are: "Outstanding," "Pure gold" and "MVP from day 1."[149]

If the task of a performance appraisal is merely to signal to decision-makers whether a particular individual should be promoted or not, the military system, in its "up is down, hot is cold" doublespeak achieves its aim.[150] But if superlatives such as "superior" and "exemplary!" that are attached to low achievers are intended to help individuals develop and improve, the military appraisal system leaves much to be desired.

360-DEGREE FEEDBACK

The performance appraisal's tendency to become a game of "Gotcha!" subject to single-rater bias spurred the development of an alternative known as 360-degree feedback. Some of the characteristics of 360-degree feedback include:

Multiple Perspectives. The boss is not the only voice heard in the feedback loop. Subordinates, peers, customers, and superiors (not the boss, but the boss's peers) contribute their perspectives on the participant's overall performance.[151] Note that the person being rated is not called an employee or subordinate, but a participant, thereby emphasizing the nonthreatening/learning tone of the exercise.

Reality Check. Multiple perspectives provide the participant with a "reality check." In chapter 6, we discussed the Johari window and how certain qualities you have as a leader are sometimes known to you, and sometimes unknown. 360-degree feedback is a tool for discovering blind spots in your leadership behavior. You think you're a smooth-talking, persuasive leader. Is that really so? What if your subordinates, peers, and bosses tell you otherwise?

Skill & Competency Focus. Instead of focusing exclusively on how well an individual performed her job, 360-degree feedback is more concerned with people skills, leadership, problem-solving, and similar intangibles. After all, the goal of feedback is not merely to help someone do their job better, but to develop the skills and knowledge needed to lift herself to the next stage in her career or a higher level of performance. 360-degree feedback centers upon developmental goals – helping people develop tools that will make them more effective contributors.[152]

Self-Improvement. By carefully considering feedback from multiple raters, and through the guidance of a coach (not one's boss), participants tailor their own personal leadership development plan. One participant decides that her communication skills need work. Another participant decides to be more inclusive when making decisions. The overall idea is that each participant sets his own learning goals for the coming year.[153] Some of the questions coaches ask participants in facilitating the feedback process and development of a personal leadership plan include:[154]

- Were you surprised by the data? Pleased? Disappointed?
- What overarching themes do you notice from the data?
- According to the data, what are your key strengths? Opportunities for development?
- What changes are you motivated to make right now?
- What changes are you motivated to pursue in the coming months?

Note for Clarity: Participants know who their raters are, but they do not know how each rater responded.

A Full Picture of Performance 360-Degree Feedback relies upon of the three main groups that encircle the participant: superiors, peers, and subordinates.

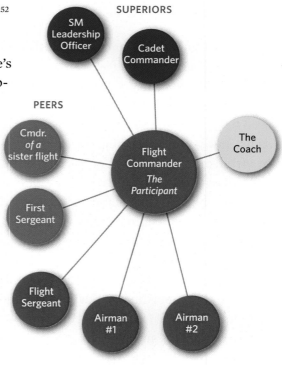

Boss Relationship. In an effort to make the feedback process as psychologically unthreatening as possible, the participant "owns" the feedback data; the boss does not even see it in its raw form.[155] Even the feedback coach (who is not the participant's boss) resists the urge to assume a position of authority. Rather, "the participants are the experts, deciding for themselves what to pay attention to and how to make meaning of the feedback."[156]

Criticism of 360-Degree Feedback. If you have to seek input from multiple people, a 360-feedback process will be time consuming. Add to it the administrative challenge of constructing some kind of confidentiality screen so that raters can give honest feedback anonymously, without their critical comments pointing back to them. Moreover, 360-degree feedback is potentially expensive. The system depends upon a highly-trained coach to facilitate the feedback meetings and help the participants draft their own personal leadership plans. (Think "expensive consultant.") Finally, critics charge that because the boss is not the final rater who passes judgment on the feedback instrument, the whole exercise has no consequences. You can bomb with every rater, yet only you and the coach will know that, so you keep your job. Defenders of 360-degree feedback would counter that bosses have other methods to communicate to an employee that they "better start performing, or else!"[157] Besides, argue the proponents of 360-degree feedback, the purpose of feedback is not to fix blame but to assist people in doing better.

MEASURING ORGANIZATIONAL PERFORMANCE

OBJECTIVES:

33. Discuss basic philosophies of measuring organizational performance.
34. Describe the difference between processes and outputs.
35. Describe the process of managing by objective.
36. Discuss pros and cons of using management by objective.

How is our team doing? What information do we need to answer that question intelligently? Just as leaders appraise the performance of individual team members, they also appraise the team's overall success. Performance measurement is a tool within the control function of management. What are some of the fundamental philosophies that surround performance measurement?

PHILOSOPHY OF ORGANIZATIONAL PERFORMANCE MEASUREMENT

Continuous Improvement. Measurement helps you improve. Metrics help you figure out if you are on track to fulfill your goals and dis-

What's measured is what matters. What's measured, is what gets done.

Measure the number of gigs during uniform inspections, tie that figure to promotins, and you'll start seeing lots of spit-shined boots.

Check homework daily, include homework in the students' overall grade, and students will complete their homework.

Monitor sales but not quality, sales will be high, but quality will be low.

Reimburse for medical tests but don't measure whether the patient actually gets healed, and you'll see lots of tests conducted without people necessarily getting healthier.

Count home runs but not strike outs, and sluggers will always swing for the fences, while striking out a lot.

cern if you are keeping up with the competition. Two proverbs of management speak to the need for performance management: "What's measured is what matters,"[158] and "If you can't measure it, you can't improve it."[159]

A System of Moving Targets. An organization is a system. It's like a machine made up of many moving parts. For this reason, measuring a team's performance is difficult because a single metric can be misleading.[160] "Profits are up!" Sounds like good news. But if the profits came at the expense of quality, perhaps the customers will get angry and go elsewhere next time. The apparent good news suggested by a single metric viewed in isolation was actually a warning sign.

92% of Statistics Lie. If leaders are not careful, their performance metrics will stand upon shaky ground. Aggregation and timeline bias are two examples. Simply put, how you group measurements together can give you a misleading picture of the whole.[161] Consider the stock market. These three charts suggest different market conditions, and yet the charts measure the same thing – an index called the S&P 500.[162] (The left-hand chart's data is a segment of the middle chart's data, which is itself a segment of the right-hand chart's data.) Look at the first chart and you'd think the market was climbing and doing great. The second chart suggests that we took a bad dip, but are climbing back out. The third chart shows good overall growth, despite some ups and downs. In short, if asked "How is the market doing?" your answer will depend upon how you aggregate the data or look at it over a certain timeline.

Be Approximately Right, Not Exactly Wrong

Although this may seem a paradox, all exact science is dominated by the idea of approximation. When a man tells you that he knows the exact truth about anything, you are safe in inferring that he is an inexact man. Every careful measurement in science is always given with the probable error... every observer admits that he is likely wrong, and knows about how much wrong he is likely to be.

— BERTRAND RUSSELL, philosopher[164]

Fine Print: You might see aggregation bias referred to as "ecological correlation" or a "level of analysis" problem.[165]

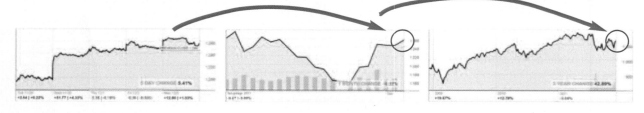

Processes vs. Outputs. You've checked the weather, you've fueled the aircraft, you've completed your preflight. Each of these accomplishments is an important activity for an aircrew, but they are *processes* that merely enable *outputs*.[163] What counts is actually flying the mission and locating the target; we measure success by asking if we have produced an output. Therefore, in measuring a team's performance, it is more important to focus upon outputs than processes.* We want to know what percent of targets we're able to find, not how many preflights we've completed. For another example, consider a cadet squadron that is required to complete an annual report of its aerospace education programs. The Red Squadron files the report on time, but the report itself basically says, "We did nothing in aerospace this year." Meanwhile, after much prodding from the wing, the Blue

*Fine Print: Outputs Yield Outcomes. Not to put too fine a point on it, but we are speaking of measuring a team's performance. Outputs are the key metrics. But above the team or operational level, strategic level leaders go a step above outputs by measuring outcomes.[166] A cadet orientation flight is an output. A cadet went flying – so what? The output matters only if it contributes to an outcome – today's young people becoming tomorrow's aerospace leaders.

What ought to count more, process or outcome?

Squadron files its report 3 months late. Their report lists dozens of awesome aerospace activities that they accomplished in the past year. Improperly focus upon processes, and you (wrongly) judge the Red Squadron as most successful. Properly focus upon outputs and you recognize the Blue Squadron sets the pace.

Benchmarking. The best source for goals is often outside the organization. Benchmarking is the process of examining the competitor's best practices and then trying to beat those measures.[167] If buying a car, which metric would be more persuasive to you? The car model that is 5% more fuel efficient than it was last year, or the car model that is the most fuel efficient available anywhere? Because the makers of the first car improved a little from last year, that irrelevant metric may give them a false sense of security. They went from awful to a little less awful. In contrast, the makers of the second car are right to be confident of their performance because their car beats all others in fuel efficiency. By looking outside their own team for goals and measures of success, teams open their eyes to levels of performance they never would have thought possible.[168]

MANAGEMENT BY OBJECTIVE

Informed by a basic philosophy on how to measure a team's performance, next we'll take a deeper look at a particular approach for determining team effectiveness. Management by objective (MBO) is a respected process for setting goals that cascade down into objectives, which, in turn, become the metrics for the team's overall success.[169] How does MBO work?

Strategic Goals. First, a good mix of senior, middle, and low-level leaders come together to set overarching goals for the team. These first-tier goals, sometimes called strategic goals, are general or abstract in nature. Consider them outcomes, to borrow the terminology discussed in the previous section. The key here is that leaders and team members jointly agree upon the goals, and the goals fairly describe what the team is trying to achieve.[170]

Objectives. Beneath each strategic goal, team leaders set sub-goals or objectives. The idea is that by completing this set of objectives, the team will naturally achieve the corresponding strategic goal. A simple, cascading logic is on display here. In contrast to the abstract strategic goals, the team objectives are specific and measurable.[171]

Action Plans. Cascading down even further to the nitty-gritty of the team's work, beneath the objectives stand action plans. These documents outline specifically who is going to do what and by when to complete the corresponding objective.[172]

Recall that earlier in the chapter we introduced MBO as a tool for measuring individual performance.

The cascade of goals, objectives, & action plans

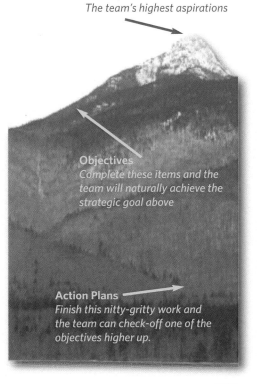

Strategic Goals
The team's highest aspirations

Objectives
Complete these items and the team will naturally achieve the strategic goal above

Action Plans
Finish this nitty-gritty work and the team can check-off one of the objectives higher up.

MBO in Action

					This metric qualifies as an "outcome."
CAP Strategic Outcome	"Dynamic Americans and aerospace leaders"				

	ITEM	BENCHMARK or RATIONALE	OWNERS	METRICS	
Squadron's Strategic Goal (One of a handful of goals)	Achieve "best of class" cadet retention	— Squadron retention last year: 51% — Top retention rate in Wing: 60% — Boy Scout retention rate in our county: 58% Our Target: 60%	Squadron Commander Cadet Commander	At least 60% of cadets on roster as of 1 January renew their membership by 31 December.	This metric qualifies as an "output."
Squadron Objectives (These five objectives will lead us toward completing the strategic goal)	1. Meeting Schedule. Produce a written schedule for each squadron meeting. Must be coordinated among staff at least one week prior to the meeting	Exit surveys show that poorly planned weekly meetings are a major demotivating factor.	Cadet Commander & Deputy Commander (as approving authority)	Yes / No, examined monthly	Objectives 1-5 are "processes."
	2. Hands On Activities. Conduct at least one "hands-on" activity during every meeting. Excludes drill.	Exit surveys show that boring, lecture-based meetings are demotivating.	Aerospace Officer & Leadership Officer & Deputy Commander (as approving authority)	Yes / No, examined monthly	
	3. Special Activities. Offer at least one "Saturday" activity every month.	Great activities keep cadets motivated to participate in CAP.	Activities Officer & Cadet Commander	Yes / No, examined monthly	
	4. Flying. Provide every cadet with at least one orientation flight per year.	Surveys show that flying is a major motivation for cadets.	Operations Officer, in cooperation with Wing HQ	Percent completion, examined quarterly	
	5. Attendance. Track attendance weekly, and reach out to cadets who have been absent a month.	Failure to attend at least one CAP event per month is a leading indicator that the cadet will choose not to renew.	Cadet XO & First Sergeant	Attendance logs & follow-up phone calls, examined monthly	

MBO AS A SCORECARD

So how do you use MBO's system of cascading goals, objectives, and action plans to measure the team's performance?

Simply write down your cascading goals and objectives, and MBO provides a scorecard for tracking the team's accomplishments. Periodically, the team gets together and evaluates the status of the various objectives, updating the scorecard as they go.[173] Which objectives have been completed? Which are almost complete? Which remain undone? Moreover,

Recall the SMART goals approach briefly discussed in chapter 10 and explained more fully in *The Cadet Staff Handbook*.

which objectives are no longer relevant and need to be adjusted, due to fast-paced changes in the team's environment? Because of the cascading nature of the MBO system, leaders can be confident that if their teams are completing their objectives, they will eventually fulfill their overall strategic goals.[174] At least that's the theory.

The respected scholar who devised MBO sees its greatest strength as "making it possible for [people] to control their own performance."[175] MBO enables leaders to "substitute management by self-control for management by domination" because each team member is empowered to complete his or her assigned objectives in whatever manner they deem best.[176]

CRITICISM OF MBO

The MBO system dates back to the early 1950s.[177] It's no longer a buzzworthy, trendy way of determining team effectiveness. Of course, defenders reply that MBO has proven its worth and will continue to outlast the next generation of fads. What is more powerful is the charge that if you lead via MBO, you'll spend too much time writing and reading reports instead of actually doing the job. Individuals responsible for completing the various objectives will feel pressured to get those objectives done and may fudge the reports to suggest the objectives have been met. Moreover, if an objective is incomplete, MBO does not tell leaders why it is incomplete or what they should do next.

Worst of all, in MBO, you're saying that one goal cascades down into certain objectives, but how can you be sure the connection is truly relevant?[178] Just because you're keeping busy does not mean you're productive. Further, in MBO, you're still looking at metrics in isolation. Critics charge that you need to find a way to consider all the important measures together in a system known as a balanced scorecard, but that system is beyond the scope of our discussion here.[179]

MEASUREMENT & THE LEADER

In his role as navigator-in-chief, the commander must carefully monitor how well individual team members and the collective group are proceeding toward their intended destinations.

Managers try to quantify their world. They try, admirably, to convert creativity, sweat, and perseverance into numbers and checkboxes on scorecards. After all, leadership is part science. But if the challenge of measuring the world seems daunting, that is because leadership remains part art as well.

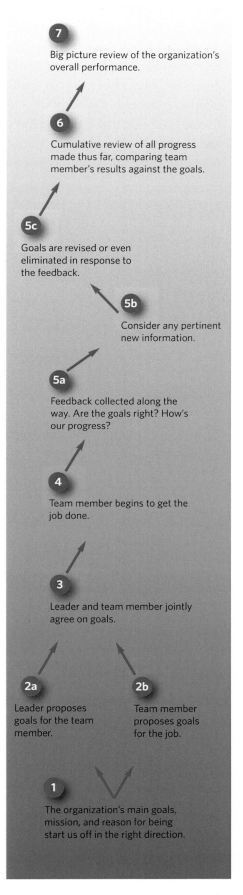

MBO in Practice
A Process Chart [180]

7 Big picture review of the organization's overall performance.

6 Cumulative review of all progress made thus far, comparing team member's results against the goals.

5c Goals are revised or even eliminated in response to the feedback.

5b Consider any pertinent new information.

5a Feedback collected along the way. Are the goals right? How's our progress?

4 Team member begins to get the job done.

3 Leader and team member jointly agree on goals.

2a Leader proposes goals for the team member.

2b Team member proposes goals for the job.

1 The organization's main goals, mission, and reason for being start us off in the right direction.

CONCLUSION

Command is the pinnacle of leadership. In this chapter, we have considered the special duties that belong to commanders alone and not other, ordinary leaders. We've examined matters like articulating a command intent and developing the team's human capital. To enlarge the commander's understanding of the full system of leadership, we studied the full range leadership model (FRLM) and principles of delegation. We discussed two other areas of leadership that properly belong on the commander's desk – leadership of the organizational culture, and the measurement of organizational effectiveness. Throughout this chapter, our theme has been that command is a leadership challenge like no other, and that among its responsibilities are areas of leadership that cannot be delegated. Having studied this diverse and challenging topic, are you ready for the challenge of command?

NOTES

1 U.S. Air Force, *Guidelines for Command*, AU-2, September 2003, 1.

2 Timothy T. Timmons, *Commanding an Air Force Squadron*, (Maxwell AFB: AU Press, 1993); followed up by Jeffry F. Smith, *Commanding an Air Force Squadron in the 21st Century*, (Maxwell AFB: AU Press, 2003).

3 Timmons, 7.

4 Ibid., 2.

5 Ibid., 10.

6 Herman Melville, *Moby Dick*, 1851, condensed from chapters XXVIII through XXX.

7 Henry David Thoreau, *Walden*, 1854, Jeffrey S. Cramer, ed., (New Haven: Yale Press, 2004), 22.

8 Timmons, 13.

9 Timmons, 11.

10 Justin Locke, "Confessions of a First-Time Manager," advisorperspectives.com, accessed November 2011.

11 Ibid., 1.

12 Peter F. Drucker, attributed by Bob Vasquez, *Heirpower! Eight Basic Habits of Exceptionally Powerful Lieutenants*, (Maxwell AFB: Air University Press, 2006), xvii.

13 Grover Furr, "Did George Washington Turn Down an Offer to Be a King?," Montclair State University, Department of English, March 2007, http://chss.montclair.edu/english/furr/gbi/docs/kingmyth.html, accessed November 2011.

14 Joseph Conrad, attributed by James Stavridis & Robert Girrier, *Command at Sea*, 6th ed., (Annapolis: Naval Institute Press, 2010), 4.

15 Bob Vasquez, 27-28.

16 Michael John Morris, *The First Time Manager*, (London: Kogan Page Ltd., 2005), 47.

17 Michael Hieb & Ulrich Schade, "Improving Planning and Re-planning...," *The International C2 Journal* 1, no. 2 (2007): 69-90.

18 David S. Alberts & Richard E. Hayes, *Understanding Command & Control, The Command & Control Research Program* (Washington: Office of the Asst. Sec. of Defense, 2006), 39.

19 Ibid., 37.

20 Ibid., 37.

21 Stavridis & Girrier, 19.

22 Ibid., 15.

23 Matt Gutman, "One Year After Haiti's Quake," ABC News, Jan 12, 2011, http://abcnews.go.com/International/haiti-year-quake-cholera-babies-school-walls/story?id=12592198#.TtUS-bGCM7x4, accessed November 2011.

24 Alberts & Hayes, 35.

25 Ibid., 38.

26 Yogi Berra, *When You Come to a Fork in the Road, Take It!* (New York: Hyperion, 2001), 53.

27 Paul Hersey, Kenneth H. Blanchard, & Dewey E. Johnson, *Management of Organizational Behavior*, 7th ed., (Upper Saddle River, NJ: Prentice Hall, 1996), 548.

28 James A. Autry, *The Servant Leader*, (New York: Three Rivers Press, 2001), 25.

29 John M. Bryson, *Strategic Planning for Public & Nonprofit Organizations*, 3rd ed., (San Francisco: Jossey-Bass, 2004), 105.

30 Autry, 28.

31 Northrop Grumman, "Our Vision, Values and Behaviors," http://www.northropgrumman.com/corporate-responsibility/ethics/our-vision-values-and-behaviors.html, accessed November 2011.

32 USAF Honor Guard, http://www.honorguard.af.mil/, accessed November 2011.

33 Autry, 28.

34 Stephen R. Covey, *Principle-Centered Leadership*, (New York: Free Press, 1991), 166.

35 Bryson, 106.

36 Ibid., 105.

37 Covey, 165.

38 Bryson, 109-111.

39 Perry M. Smith, *Rules & Tools for Leaders*, (New York: Perigree, 2002), 149.

40 Gary S. Becker, "Human Capital," *The Concise Encyclopedia of Economics*, http://www.econlib.org/library/Enc/Human Capital.html, accessed November 2011.

41 Margie Mader-Clark, *The Job Description Handbook*, 2d ed., (Berkeley CA: Nolo, 2008), 3.

42 Autry, 64.

43 Ibid., 63.

44 Ibid., 68.

45 Ibid., 67.

46 Ibid., 64.

47 Gregory P. Smith, "How to Interview and Hire Top People Every Time," Chart Your Course International, http://www.chartcourse.com/Article-Interview_question.html, accessed November 2011.

48 Louis V. Imundo, *The Effective Supervisor's Handbook*, 2nd ed., (New York: American Management Assoc., 1991), 83-84.

49 U.S. Equal Employment Opportunity Commission, "Prohibited Employment Policies/Practices," http://www.eeoc.gov/laws/practices/index.cfm, accessed November 2011.

50 Imundo, 81.

51 Gregory P. Smith.

52 Loc. cit.

53 Loc. cit.

54 Imundo, 84-85.

55 Perry M. Smith, 155.

56 Imundo, 87.

57 Comila Shahani-Denning, "Physical Attractiveness Bias in Hiring: What Is Beautiful Is Good," *Journal of Personality*, (2000), 14-17.

58 John Cawley, "Why the Overweight Earn Less," *New York Times*, "Room for Debate," November 29, 2011.

59 David J. Walsh, *Employment Law for Human Resource Practice*, 3rd ed., (Mason, OH: South-Western Cengage Learning, 2009), 104.

60 Judy Nadler & Miriam Schulman, "Favoritism, Cronyism, & Nepotism," Markkula Center for Applied Ethics, Santa Clara University, http://www.scu.edu/ethics/practicing/focusareas/government_ethics/introduction/cronyism.html.

61 Dave Nielsen, interview by author via email, Dec 19, 2011.

62 Imundo, 89.

63 Larry Bossidy, CEO of AlliedSignal / Honeywell, attributed in Kathy Shwiff, *Best Practices: Hiring People*, (New York: Harper Collins, 2007), 98.

64 Gregorio Billikopf, "Firing With Dignity," University of California at Berkeley, Agricultural Labor Management, http://www.cnr.berkeley.edu/ucce50/ag-labor/7article/article19.htm, accessed November 2011.

65 Ibid.

66 Bruce J. Avolio, "Foreword," in John J. Sosik & Don I. Jung, *Full Range Leadership Development*, (New York: Routledge, 2010), xvii.

67 James MacGregor Burns, *Transforming Leadership*, (New York: Grove Press, 2003), 2.

68 John J. Sosik & Don I. Jung, *Full Range Leadership Development*, (New York: Routledge, 2010), 10.

69 Ibid., 10.

70 Avolio, xvii.

71 Sosik & Jung, 11.

72 Ibid., 12.

73 Ibid., 13.

74 Loc. cit.

75 MacGregor Burns, 24.

76 Peter G. Northouse, *Leadership Theory and Practice*, (Thousand Oaks, Calif: Sage Publications, 2001), 132.

77 Sosik & Jung, 18.

78 David Letterman, *The Late Show with David Letterman*, September 17, 2011.

79 Sosik & Jung, 17.

80 Ibid., 16.

81 Ibid., 15.

82 Ibid., 67.

83 AFJROTC, *Leadership Education IV: Principles of Management*, (Maxwell AFB, AL: Air University, 1999), 112-123.

84 Attributed.

85 Elisabeth Bumiller, "Casualty of Firestorm: Outrage, Bush, & FEMA Chief," *New York Times*, September 10, 2005.

86 Bill Clinton, address to the nation, August 17, 1998, via transcript published in *New York Times*, August 18, 1998.

87 Barack Obama, address to nation, May 1, 2011, via *New York Times*, May 1, 2011.

88 William Safire, "In Event of Moon Disaster," draft of speech for Richard Nixon, http://www.archives.gov/press/press-kits/american-originals.html#nixon, accessed February 2012.

89 Google, "The Google Culture," http://www.google.com/intl/en/about/corporate/company/culture.html, accessed Nov. 2011.

90 Edgar H. Schein, *Organizational Culture and Leadership*, 4th ed., (San Francisco: Jossey-Bass, 2010), 24.

91 Afsaneh Nahavandi, *The Art and Science of Leadership*, (Upper Saddle River, NJ: Prentice Hall, 2003), 7.

92 Loc. cit.

93 James Roughton & James Mercurio, *Developing an Effective Safety Culture: A Leadership Approach*, (Woburn, MA: Butterworth-Heinemann, 2002), 29.

94 Shel Holz & John C. Havens, *Tactical Transparency*, (San Francisco: Jossey-Bass, 2009), 37.

95 Ibid., 9.

96 Loc. cit.

97 James Howard Kunstler, "Eyesore of the Month," March 2010, http://www.kunstler.com/eyesore_201003.html, accessed November 2011.

98 Heraclitus, DK B119.

99 Schein, 300 ff.

100 Chronology of al-Qaida attacks is from *Frontline*, "The Man Who Knew: al-Qaida's Global Context," http://www.pbs.org/wgbh/pages/frontline/shows/knew/etc/cron.html, accessed November 2011.

101 Leon Panetta, "Statement on... Repeal of Don't Ask, Don't Tell," DoD News Release No. 644-11, July 22, 2011, http://www.defense.gov/releases/release.aspx?releaseid=14681.

102 Schein, 302.

103 Price Pritchett & Ron Pound, *High-Velocity Culture Change*, (Dallas: Pritchett, LP), 11.

104 Hal G. Rainey, *Understanding & Managing Public Organizations*, 3rd ed., (San Francisco: Jossey-Bass, 2003), 312.

105 Peter F. Drucker, *Management*, Revised ed., (New York: Harper Business, 2008), 9.

106 Jean M. Twenge, *Generation Me*, (New York: Free Press, 2006), 44 & 51.

107 Schein, 306.

108 Ibid., 311.

109 Pritchett, 22.

110 S.J. Diamond, "Not All Stores Will Cheerfully Give Refunds," *Los Angeles Times*, December 15, 1986.

111 The explanation of internalization is based on Krathwohl's taxonomy of the affective domain. For a brief summary, see Don Clark, "Taxonomy of Learning Domains," at http://www.nwlink.com/~donclark/hrd/bloom.html.

112 Pritchett, 22.

113 Schein, 312.

114 Title 15 U.S.C., Chapter 6 §(204) 205a - 205l, *Metric Conversion Law*, December 23, 1975.

115 Pritchett, 32.

116 John P. Kotter, "Leading Change," in *Harvard Business Review on Change*, (Boston: Harvard Business School Press, 1998), 7.

117 Ralph Waldo Emerson, "Self-Reliance," 1841.

118 Paul Strebel, "Why Do Employees Resist Change?" in *Harvard Business Review on Change*, (Boston: Harvard Business School Press, 1998), 142.

119 Ibid., 143.

120 Ibid., 151.

121 Pritchett, 22.

122 Roughton & Mercurio, 17.

123 American Institute of Chemical Engineers (AIChE), "Safety Culture: What Is At Stake?," http://www.aiche.org/uploaded-Files/CCPS/Resources/KnowledgeBase/Whats_at_stake_Rev1.pdf, accessed November 2011.

124 Stavridis & Girrier, 14.

125 AIChE, 1.

126 Roughton & Mercurio, 22.

127 International Atomic Energy Agency, "Frequently Asked Chernobyl Questions," http://www.iaea.or.at/newscenter/features/chernobyl-15/cherno-faq.shtml, accessed Nov. 2011.

128 John Bernard Taylor, *Safety Culture: Assessing & Changing the Behaviour of Organisations*, (Surrey, England: Gower Publishing, 2010), 2.

129 Theodore Roosevelt Association, "Pure Food and Drug Act," http://www.theodoreroosevelt.org/life/PureFoodDrug.htm, accessed November 2011.

130 Sinclair Lewis, *The Jungle*, 1906, chapter 14.

131 AIChE, 2.

132 Roughton & Mercurio, 23.

133 Sandy Smith, "VPPPA Supports OSHA's Position on Incentive Programs," EHS Today, October 3, 2010, http://ehstoday.com/safety/incentives/vpppa-supports-osha-position-incentive-program-4454/, accessed November 2011.

134 Roughton & Mercurio, 26.

135 Ibid., 30.

136 Attributed in Wilfred J. Kaydos, *Operational Performance Measurement*.

137 Imundo, 160.

138 Ibid., 161.

139 Peter F. Drucker, *Management Challenges for the 21st Century*, (New York: HarperCollins, 1999), 142 ff.

140 Imundo, 167.

141 Ibid., 168.

142 Drucker (2008), xxix.

143 Pauline Rennie Peyton, *Dignity at Work: Eliminate Bullying & Create a Positive Work Environment*, (New York: Brunner-Routledge, 2003), 129.

144 John W. Fleenor, et al., *Leveraging the Impact of 360-Degree Feedback*, Center for Creative Leadership, (San Francisco: Pfeiffer, 2008), xvii.

145 Imundo, 165.

146 Manuel London, *Job Feedback: Giving, Seeking, & Using Feedback for Performance Improvement*, 2d ed., (Mahwah, NJ: Lawrence Erlbaum Assoc., 2008).

147 Peyton, 129.

148 Society of Armed Forces Medical Laboratory Scientists, "Officer Performance Reports: You on a Piece of Paper," http://www.safmls.org/2008/2008%20Presentations/Officer%20Performance%20Reports%20(OPR).ppt, accessed Nov. 2011.

149 *Air Force Writer*, "How to Sabotage the Promotion Statement," http://www.airforcewriter.com/secret2.htm, accessed November 2011.

150 Ibid.

151 John W. Fleenor, et al., 2.

152 Ibid., 17.

153 Ibid., 5.

154 Ibid., 51.

155 Ibid., 4.

156 Ibid., 51.

157 John W. Fleenor & Stéphane Brutus, "Multisource Feedback for Personnel Decisions," in T*he Handbook of Multisource Feedback*, (San Francisco: Jossey-Bass, 2001), 349.

158 Gwyn Bevan & Christopher Hood, "What's measured is what matters," *Public Administration* 84, no. 3 (2006): 517-538.

159 Attributed to Peter F. Drucker by *MarketCulture*, blog.marketculture.com.

160 Stacey Barr, "Ten Biggest Mistakes in Managing Organisational Performance," http://www.staceybarr.com/freeinfo/articles/MeasurementMistakes.pdf, accessed November 2011.

161 Edward Tufte, "Aggregate Evidence," *ET Notebooks*, (Dec. 20, 2006), http://www.edwardtufte.com/bboard/q-and-a-fetch-msg?msg_id=0002ba, accessed November 2011.

162 S&P 500 charts from *CNN Money*, http://money.cnn.com/data/markets/sandp/, accessed December 2011.

163 Office of Management & Budget, "Performance Measurement Challenges & Strategies," (June 18, 2003), http://www.whitehouse.gov/sites/default/files/omb/part/challenges_strategies.pdf, accessed November 2011.

164 Bertrand Russell, *The Scientific Outlook*, 1931, (New York: Routledge, 2001), 42.

165 Barr, op. cit.

166 Office of Management & Budget.

167 Robert G. Eccles, "The Performance Management Manifesto," (1991), in *Harvard Business Review on Measuring Corporate Performance*, (Boston: HBS Press, 1998), 32.

168 Loc. cit.

169 Hal G. Rainey, *Understanding & Managing Public Organizations*, 3rd ed., (San Francisco: Jossey-Bass, 2003), 136.

170 Hersey, Blanchard, & Johnson, 159.

171 Bryson, 282.

172 Loc. cit.

173 Hersey, Blanchard, & Johnson, 159.

174 Loc. cit.

175 Drucker (2008), 266.

176 Loc. cit.

177 Hersey, Blanchard, & Johnson, 158.

178 Barr, op. cit.

179 Robert S. Kaplan & David P. Norton, "The Balanced Scorecard," (1992), in *Harvard Business Review on Measuring Corporate Performance*, (Boston: HBR Press, 1998), 127.

180 Based upon Hersey, Blanchard, & Johnson, 160.

PHOTOS & PERMISSIONS

All photos are from Civil Air Patrol or public domain sources, unless noted otherwise.

INDEX

MCREL EDUCATIONAL STANDARDS

The *Learn to Lead* curriculum is correlated to Midcontinent Research for Education and Learning (McREL) standards for life skills, behavioral studies, career education, language arts, and civics. McREL maintains standards documents from professional subject area organizations and selected state governments. By referencing the McREL standards, the Learn to Lead curriculum demonstrates content relevance in the eyes of independent subject matter experts. For details, please see the *Learn to Lead Curriculum Guide* and capmembers.com/learntolead.

McREL standards are copyright 2010 by McREL

Mid-continent Research for Education and Learning
4601 DTC Blvd., Suite 500
Denver, CO 80237
Telephone: 303/337/0990
mcrel.org/standards-benchmarks

Used with permission.

Photo courtesy of the family

The LEARN TO LEAD series
is dedicated to the memory of
Lance Corporal **JEFFREY S. HOLMES** USMC,
a former cadet from New Hampshire Wing
who grew from a small, uncertain cadet into
a strong man and a Marine,
all the while keeping his infectiously cheerful attitude.
He was killed in action on Thanksgiving Day, 2004,
during the Battle for Fallujah, Iraq.
He was 20 years old.
Requiescat in pace.

Appreciations

WE WAITED FOR OUR RIDE IN THE PITCH BLACK, 4:30 in the morning, and it was wicked cold. I climbed into the back of a pickup truck en route to Wing Headquarters for my first sarex. Nearly thirty years later, from the Deep South of all places, here I am thanking a great team for incredible support upon our completing *Learn to Lead.*

Looking back, it's bewildering to realize that the text you are holding was but a dream that **Rob Smith** and **Dr. Jeff Montgomery** and I sketched out at lunch one day. I remember that lunch well: I had a grilled cheese. Rob and Jeff helped with volumes 1 and 2, but not 3 and 4, yet still they top my list. Thank you.

Everyone on our growing Cadet Team contributed to the volume 3 and 4 effort. My thanks to **Joe Curry** who is now an expert on getting permissions for photos of Yoda, the poetry of Langston Hughes, sixty-year old articles by Tooey Spaatz, or just about any intellectual property a leadership textbook could need. **Margaret Probst,** our intrepid DDR specialist, kept so much of the day-to-day business afloat while others focused on L2L. As he did with the earlier volumes, **Neil Probst** distinguished himself as a key contributor, particularly in preparing volume 4's collection of readings. He's one of the finest copy editors you'll find. Moreover, he's been the workhorse behind the written tests and online systems that augment these texts. Our rookie education manager, **Becci Sundhagen,** hit home runs every time at bat. Her fingerprints are all over the good stuff you find in volumes 3 and 4. I'm indebted to her for helping us make connections across chapters, for making sense out of some half-formed ideas we had for volume 4, and for great service in editing. **Steven Trupp** helped with permissions, editing, vetting test questions, and a dozen other tasks that sprang up. As a long-time field guy and DCP, Steven was always ready with intelligent perspectives from the cadets' and seniors' points of view.

Throughout this long process my bosses **Jim Mallett** and **Don Rowland** provided every last resource and bit of encouragement we could ever want, while giving me free reign to take L2L where I wanted to go. Thank you, sirs.

Once again, **Barb Pribulick** came to our aid with vital Quark and Photoshop support, and her boss in Creative Services, **Jim Tynan,** ensured the physical book you're holding would be a high-quality glossy treasure.

Three outside consultants came to our rescue. Dr. **Kalynne Pudner,** a visiting professor at Auburn University, reminded me that my knowledge of ethics was pretty rusty, and helpfully corrected more technical inaccuracies than I care to admit. **Capt Chad Grondahl,** a flight commander at the USAF Squadron Officer College and longtime CAP member, brought a wealth of subject matter expertise to the effort – our Jeter coming off the bench. **Dr. Ashley Davis** crafted a huge bank of multiple choice test questions.

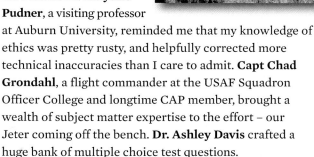

Anyone who is the least bit familiar with CAP knows that the organization's real work is not done in Gill Robb Wilson Hall but in the airport hangars, church basements, and gymnasiums where cadets meet on Tuesday night. We collected innumerable great ideas from the conference circuit and our friends online. My thanks to the dedicated **Cadet Programs Officers** and **Cadet Advisory Councils** in the field for their expertise. Most especially, my former volunteer counterpart, **Lt Col Ned Lee,** and current counterpart, **Col Craig Treadwell,** tirelessly championed L2L throughout. It's a pleasure working with guys whose hearts are as pure as their minds are wise.

My buddy **Major Jason Smith** always offered great advice and feedback during our long phone calls. Whenever I work a cadet project, I ask for Jason's input.

Most of all, I say that that girl who married me for some strange reason, **Amanda,** made it all possible. She's a tremendous editor and counselor, and now according to the toddler who patrols our home, a perfect mom, too.

Regardless of this mighty arsenal of brainpower, any shortcomings with the curriculum or errors of any sort that remain are the fault of yours truly.

If you're a cadet and you're reading this, know that yesterday's generation of cadets wants you to become the leaders America needs you to be. We're confident that, aided in small part by L2L, you will set the new standard.

Semper Vigilans,
Curt La Fond